A JOURNEY OF HOPE

By members of the HOPE Cancer Support Group

Dedication

To all those, whose lives have been and continue to be affected by cancer, either directly or indirectly. In memory of all former members of the HOPE Cancer Support Group, two of whom contributed to the work of this book. A special mention goes to Alex Lineham, whose courageous battle ended in September 2010. Alex worked hard and with great commitment in the process of compiling this book. She encouraged every one of us with her strength and determination to make each day count and live life to the full in the face of uncertainty.

Published 2011 by the HOPE Generic Cancer Support Group

©2011 HOPE Generic Cancer Support Group and the contributors

ISBN 978-0-9569032-0-4

Designed by April Sky Design, Newtownards, www.aprilsky.co.uk

Printed by GPS Colour Graphics Limited

Contents

Acknowledgements

A Journey of Hope is a collective effort of members of the HOPE Generic Cancer Support Group. Kathy Cash, co-founder and facilitator of the group, would like to give enormous thanks to all the contributors for their courage and invaluable support in compiling this book – without them, it would not have been possible. Special thanks go to Leo McGarry and Joanne Miles, who together supported and encouraged each contributor by arranging a six-week course in creative writing. This was of invaluable help to us all in the process of putting our personal experiences into words.

On behalf of all members of the Hope Cancer Support Group, we would also like to give our heartfelt thanks to all those who have given their time, encouragement and support. Without them the publication of *A Journey Of Hope* would not have been possible.

In particular, we would like to thank:
- Dr Wesley Johnston of April Sky Design: a gentleman who gave us guidance throughout the process of the publication.
- Susan Feldstein of the Feldstein Agency: our editor and a lovely lady who showed empathy for our work.
- Ards Borough Council for their support with funding towards the cost of the publication.
- All our wide circle of family and friends who never fail to support us with all their fundraising efforts and without whom we would not have reached our goal.

Thank you all for helping to make our dream a reality.

"Cancer is Not a Gift, but a Lesson"

On Wednesday 19 May 2010 the 'Cancer Journey' Writing Group in Newtownards collectively composed the following list of lessons from their individual cancer experiences:

Acceptance

We're not invincible

To look after yourself

It affects everyone/all

The ripple is widespread

To share experiences

Strength

You're not alone

Survival

Faith

The true meaning of empathy

Knowledge of cancer

To find out your real friends

We all need to look to ourselves

To know who we really are

Vulnerability

Time is precious - enjoy!

The good in people

Do not put off until tomorrow what you can do today

Focus on moving forward

Appreciation of life

Life is a journey - cancer is a part of it

You can never say "this won't happen to me"

Hope!

I'm Not Sick, I'm Normal!

Lynn Johnston
Cervical Cancer, 2003

I dedicate my story and my life to my granddaughter, Codie, who gave me the strength to get through each day. To my family and special friends, Ray, Susan and Sandra, who all supported me relentlessly and let me do it 'my way'.

I've always been an independent, free spirit, someone who speaks their mind and has done what I wanted, irrespective of the consequences – something which got me into lots of trouble in my formative years. I've never had any sort of organisation or routine to my life.

My life before cancer was somewhat chaotic – like a train lurching from side to side on an uneven track, with the highs and lows of the inclines and downhill rushes of life. At some point I had to come to a standstill, and then sure enough, I came off the rails and – crash! – the 'big C' got me . . .

Here I was in my complete naivety, sitting discussing some test results with my consultant. I was aware that all was not well with my body, but I never dreamed as to what extent. The doctor casually asked if I had come with anyone that day. 'Yes,' I replied. (I was with my then partner and a friend's young son, who I was looking after for the day). He suggested I might like to bring them into the room. Again, blissfully unaware of the significance of his request, I agreed.

I remember a nurse standing by the door with a box of tissues in hand, and wondering what she was doing. The realisation hit me, when the consultant took my hand and told me they had discovered a large tumour which required immediate attention. I was trying to keep some sense of control, as the horror and fear welled up inside me. How could I tell my two sons? What about my baby granddaughter? How would my family ever cope with this? I had so many thoughts rushing through my head in those split seconds. My life as I knew it was collapsing around me. Strangely, my main concern at this point was not to fall apart in front of the little boy that I was supposed to be looking after, and to behave as normally as possible.

This pattern of not being seen to fall apart continued throughout my treatment. From that point on, I lost control of my life, my destiny, my body, my sanity and self-respect. Gone was my independence and for the foreseeable future, the cloud of cancer was to hang over me.

Then came the problem of having to endure drastic and invasive treatment and its horrible side effects. I tried to deal with this in my own particular way. Each person has to try to handle and manage this to suit themselves: some turn to faith, some have other crutches. What I did raised a few eyebrows and some disapproval, and whilst accepted by, was in no way condoned by the medical professionals. I had been a casual, recreational user of cannabis before I got ill and it was to this that I turned. I vividly remember sitting with other patients in the smokers' area of the hospital and quietly being stoned (or perhaps not so quietly, for others around me!). This worked for me and helped dull the pain and psychological effects of the treatment. I have found that at times of stress, using cannabis in this way has kept me on an even keel. When I discussed this method of coping with my care team, they would not condone it – rightly so – but, as far as I was concerned, if it worked for me, so be it.

Whether I was in denial, I'm not really sure, but I was determined that if I kept it together and looked normal, no one would treat me or see me as sick. And so, the mask went on. Looking back now, my way of behaving was quite manic. I would get my 'I'm fine' face on first thing every morning, find the highest heels and the tightest jeans, and the act would begin.

I would go through the routine of going to hospital for scans and the preparation for my forthcoming treatment, and meeting the team at Belvoir who would be looking after me – and all the time, I was thinking, this really couldn't be for real. I decided very early on that the only way through this nightmare was not to cry. I've spent most of my life laughing at everything, and, if cancer could control all the other aspects of my life, it certainly wasn't getting hold of my sense of humour. And so most of my tears fell through laughter and total disbelief at this new, organised, routine-led rebel, who had to do everything she was told for the first time in her life!

Don't get me wrong: there were times when I did fall apart, usually in the dark of night time, when no one was around to see me – and then I would get angry for feeling sorry for myself, when I was the one causing so much pain to my family.

On my bad days, I just had to have my 'Codie hit'. This was when I held my granddaughter and I knew I could overcome anything. Most days, my head would be in overdrive. I'm sure your brain under stress goes into a natural mechanism to slow you down, as on a few occasions (which I referred to as my 'out-of-body experiences'), I actually felt as if I was walking alongside someone else. These moments were more than welcome, as they gave me a great sense of calm and well-being.

Chemotherapy and radiotherapy were naturally a big fear for me, and on my first morning of going to hospital for treatment, I must admit I was literally bouncing off the walls, believing that 'I just couldn't do this'. But, as always, my friend Susan supported me through the difficult times. The nurses were great and explained everything each step of the way.

It was the strangest experience, to feel the steroids travel round my body and passing through my head like pins and needles, before eventually it was time for me to be hooked up to the dreaded chemo drip. This drip and I just didn't get along: I was forever tripping over it, getting tangled in the wire, forgetting to plug it in, setting alarms off. But no matter what, that damned drip followed me everywhere, as I teetered around in my high heels, trying to look normal.

My brain was whizzing and my body was tired from the treatment, but I refused to give in to exhaustion. Sleeping tablets didn't work for me, so, whilst everyone was in bed sleeping, I would be in the smokers' room with my friend Ray till the early hours, eating chocolate-top buns (which, for some reason, I took mad cravings for!) and smoking God knows how many cigarettes. The nurses gave up telling me to sleep and got used to me walking around at night, usually acquiring food out of the hospital fridges, as I was always hungry. I didn't want to put pyjamas on, as I had got it into my head that pyjamas would turn me into a patient, and I was having none of that. Each morning the porter would come and get me for my radiotherapy slot and I just hated to see that wheelchair.

To me, it was another symbol of being sick. I would never get into it, and would always opt for being escorted on foot, with a kindly porter on one side and my chemo drip on the other. God – I must have been such an awkward patient!

Radiotherapy looked frightening, but once I knew it wasn't going to hurt, I was fine. My friend and I were sitting waiting for the radiologist one morning and she casually asked me what I really disliked. 'Earwigs,' I said laughing. This friend decided that this was what we would call my tumour. Every day the radiotherapy would be incinerating the 'earwig' on the inside, and on the outside I looked 'normal'.

Thankfully, I got through my treatment very well and went into remission. I remember thinking that cancer was now behind me and I could get back to the old me. I quickly learned however that when cancer touches your life, it doesn't go away. It may slip into the background but, like it or not, it is now part of your life. As with all cancer patients in remission, I sometimes dwelt on the brooding prospect of the illness reappearing. Was it away for good? Would it return? What was the cause of that pain, lump, or strange sensation? With other illnesses, once a person is cured, very little attention is devoted to the possibility of the problem recurring, but with cancer, there is always the fear that it is back. This is one of the hardest things I have found to deal with over time and, whilst I have the highest respect for the work of the specialist cancer unit, I do feel that it is easy to drop through the net of the aftercare and rehabilitation support system.

Now, seven years on, I'm doing great. My two sons have grown up and I now have two gorgeous granddaughters.

Life goes on, and for now, cancer has blended into the background of my life again.

Lynn Johnston
Cervical Cancer, 2003

This is a poem Lynn received from a friend:

Lynn's Battle
Everything changed in a split second that day.
You wished that you could run away,
And through the pain, you thought life would never feel normal again.
You faced your battle with determination and hope
And taught others round you how to cope.
You smiled, laughed and would not show others your fear;
You would not even show anyone your tears.
You were an inspiration to others who gained from your strength,
Your personality shone wherever you went.
As a friend, I have never felt so proud:
To come through this battle with you, was a privilege, to be allowed.
I have learned so much I will never forget,
You are a lifelong friend I am lucky to have met.
I know the weeks and months ahead might be hard
But your determination and strength will see you through.
You are a winner, Lynn, in everything you do.
I have said it many times before:
You are a special person
And you will always come through.

Love,
Susan

My Crossroads

Kathy Cash
Bowel Cancer, 2003

I had faced many challenges and stood at many crossroads throughout my life, but none as difficult or frightening as what I was now about to experience. The date of 13 November 2003 will always be etched in my mind, never to be forgotten, along with the memory of the expression on the doctor's face and the tone of his voice as he spoke those words: 'I am sorry to have to tell you that the diagnosis is not good. You have bowel cancer.' I knew from that moment that my life would change forever, as I took the first steps on my cancer journey.

But before I share the story of my cancer journey with you, I think it is important that you should know a little about me the person. My name is Kathy Cash, christened 'Kathleen' (my mother never called me by the shorter version). I grew up in a family of five brothers and three sisters, so there was never a dull moment. Times were difficult for my parents, especially my mother. Raising a large bunch of children was no easy task. From an early age, I discovered that life would always throw up its challenges. My mother was my mentor then, and though she sadly passed away twelve years ago, I can still hear her words today: 'Whatever life leaves at your feet, deal with it the best you can, with strength and courage, and move on.'

For every challenge, you can find a solution.

Leaving school at 15 and going into factory work was not what I wanted to do, but there were no choices then. I had to do what my brothers and sisters were doing, and that was to earn a living. Settling into the work routine was made easier by the fact that two of my sisters worked in the same factory and I was supported by them through my early days there. My sister Margaret and I worked on the stitching machines, and my sister May was a supervisor (she never let us away with anything – we had to work harder than the rest!).

Life is a succession of lessons which must be lived to be understood.

At the age of eighteen, I married Jack, and for better or worse, we will celebrate our Ruby (40th) wedding anniversary in 2011. Jack was serving with the Royal Engineers in Germany when we married, and our eldest daughter Jacqueline was born there. One month before Jacqueline was born, my mother travelled to Germany to be with me. She had never travelled anywhere alone before, so to make that journey shows a little of the strong person she was. I believe that it was my mother who moulded me to be the strong person I am today. When my mother returned to Ireland, I was unaware that she was ill, as she never complained, just carried on as normal. That is what she always did. One month after her return home, I too travelled back to Ireland with Jacqueline. The return journey to Germany never happened, as I decided not to go back. Jack understood why I made this decision and he too returned to Ireland three months later, having bought himself out of the army. I would reflect on this decision over the years to come, but never with regret.

We settled into civvy life again with its ups and downs, trying to build a home from scratch. I often think back to that time, when we were grateful to those who supported us. One year later, our second daughter Pamela was born and life settled into a routine of work and family.

Sometimes the road of life may seem to be a bit bumpy,
But it's just a small part of the great journey we are on.

I had always planned to go back to school to learn new skills when the girls had got a little older. This never happened however, as our son Jonathan was born when Pamela was ten. It would be another fifteen years before I would go back to study new skills. I had left the factory work behind and had gone on to work in retail. This change started with part-time shop work and, with great determination to prove I was capable of much more, I gradually worked my way up to management level. Having my mother to look after the children helped make this possible.

Jack and I had always dreamed of owning our own home and when Jonathan was one year old, we fulfilled that dream. It was wonderful, moving into our beautiful three-bedroom bungalow. The first few years were difficult, as we could not afford a car and the girls had to walk two miles to school through all weathers. We had to make sacrifices to enable us to realise our dream. I believe making these decisions taught the children valuable lessons which they have been able to draw upon in their own lives ever since.

> *You hold the key to your own future:*
> *You are the only one with the power to make your life all it can be.*
> *There will be difficult challenges and changes to face,*
> *But you are a courageous person.*
> *Fear is such a small word that, once faced, will lose its power to*
> *hold you back:*
> *Just take each challenge one step at a time and refuse to give up.*
> *Believe in yourself, and don't let the opinions of others influence*
> *your actions or decisions,*
> *You are the key to your future –*
> ***Make it the best it can be.***

(From *The Irish Get Up and Go Diary 2010* by Glenda Devlin, Chicco)

My next decision was to be one of the most rewarding I have ever made. Again, I was taking on a new career. This opportunity came unexpectedly, through my role as a member of the St John Ambulance, when one of the officers suggested I apply for work as a nursing auxiliary in the local hospital. This sowed a seed, and I decided I was going to give it my best shot. Following the interviews, I was overjoyed to be accepted and looked forward to this new beginning. Once the training period was over, I was told I was to become part of the staff at Ards Hospital, on the Gynae Ward. This was great news, as it meant I did not have to travel: I could walk to work and save on the travel expenses.

> *Do not run through life so fast that you forget not only where*
> *you've been, but also where you're going –*
> *Life is not a race, but a **journey**, to be savoured each step of*
> *the way.*

My early experience working on the Gynae Ward would take me on a journey into the unknown, which by the twists of fate would also one day help to give me the strength to face my own fears – the fears which would arise from my diagnosis of cancer.

In the first few months of my new job, I was learning many new skills. The staff were all supportive of each other and I settled into the routine very quickly, enjoying every day to the full. I often reflect on that time now, when I was naïve and thought that this was a nice ward to work on – that I would not have to witness death there, as others did on various other wards. This was soon to change, though. My first experience of death on the Gynae Ward was a tremendous shock to me, one I will never forget. I had helped nurse a lady there for weeks, knowing she had cancer but not believing the end would come as it did. This affected me so much, I spoke with the sister–in-charge about my feelings. I will always remember her words of response: 'Kathy,' she said, 'you must decide if you have the strength and courage to face the loss of other patients, because this will happen many times.' I knew at that moment that I could not walk away. This was where I was meant to be.

> *Do not give up when you still have something to give.*
> *Nothing is really over until the moment you stop trying.*

From that day, I gave every patient all the care, kindness and understanding that I could. I was privileged to have met so many wonderful, strong, courageous people. Memories of them would come back to me as I too faced the fears they had faced before me. In those years of caring for patients who faced so much emotional and physical trauma, I believed I had a good understanding of how they felt. How wrong I was! The truth of understanding only came to me in the moment I made those first unsteady steps on my own cancer journey.

> *Empathy is better than sympathy.*

My role in Gynae was coming to an end, as the Ards Hospital was to close and all ward staff were moving to the Ulster Hospital. Once again

I was facing change. I applied for the role of nursing auxiliary in Ards Outpatients, which was not facing the move to the Ulster. My mother's health was poor at this time and I wanted to be close by if she needed me. Again, I was lucky to be accepted for the post and with time I adjusted to the change. I worked regular hours, from Monday to Friday: no more shift work or weekend duty. My role within Outpatients was so different to my work on the wards and I missed the hands-on work, but I was eager to learn new skills and get involved in the clinics. Again I would experience the issues surrounding cancer, this time from a different side. I would now become familiar with all a patient would have to go through from the first stage of tests to a diagnosis. This terrible disease had devastating effects on so many lives, I could see that. All I could do was to give support and encouragement. I often wished I could do more.

> *Beautiful people do not just happen.*
> *The most beautiful people we have known are those who have*
> *known defeat, known suffering,*
> *Known struggle, known loss, and have found their way out of the*
> *depths.*
> *These people have an appreciation, a sensitivity and an*
> *understanding of life that fills them with compassion, gentleness,*
> *and a deep loving concern.*

My life was about to undergo more change, when Jack talked about us moving house. I was not happy with this thought, as we had been in our bungalow for fifteen happy years. Our son Jonathan was, however, the only one at home with us now, as our eldest daughter was married and our younger daughter had her own home. I put off the move for a while, but Jack had his heart set on moving to a house, as he wanted a change from the bungalow. So once again, life threw up a challenge. 'What the heck! Let's do it,' I said. So when everything was finalised, we moved in the late spring of 1998 to a beautiful three-bedroom house, with a master bedroom with en suite bathroom and loads of extra space: a new chapter in our lives.

> *All dreams can come true if you really want them to.*

This dream was to be short-lived however, as two months after moving into our dream home, I was admitted to hospital for gynae surgery. I had the surgery on the Monday and my mother came to visit me on the Wednesday. It was to be the last time I would see her beautiful, smiling face. She died on the Sunday morning of that week, two hours before I got home. My world fell apart. Nothing mattered at that moment. My mother was gone from my life, and part of me had gone with her. I felt I would never be whole again.

Nothing lasts forever.

This period of my life would throw up many difficult challenges for me. The loss of my mother left an enormous void in my life. I had felt I had fallen into a black pit and could find no way out. I could feel only pain and loneliness. Many times I tried to climb from that black pit, as I know that is what my mother would have wanted me to do. I often slipped back, but I never gave up hope that with time I would reach where I wanted to be again. Returning to work was to be my saviour as I tried to deal with my loss.

> *Believe in tomorrow.*
> *Sometimes it gets so hard to focus on what's really important*
> *in our lives.*
> *Sometimes our hearts misplace the passion for dreams, and*
> *doubt seems to take over our plans –*
> *Compromising the future we long to see.*
> *These emotions that confuse us or set us back are not signs of*
> *weakness, they are signs of our humanity, and accepting their*
> *existence is a strength we can all call upon.*

My new home became like a prison to me. I hated it. Jack and the children tried to reassure me that in time I would accept it more, but my heart knew that this house would never be home for me. I had already shed too many tears in it. After two years of trying to settle, we decided that another home would be best for me. The house was placed on the market and sold very quickly. As I looked around it on our final day there,

I felt only relief at leaving. As I glanced out the conservatory window at the beautiful garden I had tended, a lone butterfly fluttered past. This gave me hope and a feeling of comfort. But where would my life go from here? We had not found another house – although we looked at many, I just couldn't find what I was looking for. For almost a year, we lived in rented accommodation. On reflection it was more difficult for Jack and Jonathan, as they had loved our previous house. As far as I was concerned, I was just waiting for direction on the choice I was to make regarding a home. I no longer wanted a house with all the trimmings. I needed whatever would bring some contentment back into my life.

Know what you want and continue wanting it.

Circumstances were about to change and direct me onto the path I now believe was meant to be. One of my brothers had been taken seriously ill and needed a liver transplant. He lived with his wife and family in the house I had grown up in. It was as I called to visit him on a regular basis that I felt an inner need to live back in the area where I grew up. This was a decision I have never regretted making. I found peace. The crossroads was now behind me. I had found my direction for the present.

Happiness cannot be travelled to, owned, earned, worn or consumed.
Happiness is the spiritual experience of living every minute with love, grace and gratitude.

My Cancer Journey

The summer of 2003 started with my husband and I making plans to visit our eldest daughter and son-in-law in England. I had been looking forward to this break. Working full-time as a nursing auxiliary was rewarding but also hard-going, and I felt the need for some relaxation. I had been feeling exhausted. When this unexplained tiredness came on, it was debilitating, so I had been to my GP for a check-up and she had run some routine blood tests, all of which came back negative.

I assumed I was just pushing myself too hard and decided to change the dates of our break to England and go earlier than we had planned. So in the second week of August 2003, my husband and I left for England. All was going well, until one day when we were about to go out sightseeing, I went to the bathroom and passed a blood clot. My daughter asked if I was okay as she noticed my colour was poor. I said nothing other than that I was feeling a little tired.

Our holiday over, I returned to work. The blood clot episode did not worry me, as I put it down to maybe a haemorrhoid, however each time I went to the bathroom, I checked for further bleeding. As the weeks went by, I began to notice further changes in my bowel motions and as the fatigue was getting worse, I made an appointment to see my GP again. The doctor asked if she could do an examination, the result of which was an urgent referral to see a specialist. At the time I was working in Outpatients and spoke with the surgical consultant regarding my referral. I had great confidence in this consultant, and when he said he would arrange a colonoscopy as soon as he could, my words to him were, 'There's no rush. I don't think it's anything sinister.'

How wrong I was.

On the morning of Thursday, 13 November 2003, I was told I had bowel cancer.

I felt I was at a crossroads again, thinking only of my family and how I could protect them. The road I decided to take that day was with a strength and courage I did not know I had, but take it I did. My sister May, who had dropped me off that morning, returned to pick me up. There is no easy way to explain what I felt in my heart as the doctor spoke with her. As I have said, I come from a large family, with five brothers and three sisters. Both my parents were dead and this sister was now the mother figure. Together we left the hospital: my sister with information regarding what was to happen next, and me with thoughts of my husband and children. That evening was one of the hardest for me to bear. As I watched the faces of my children, all I could see was their fear. I spoke to them all and said, 'I cannot do this without your strength.' I could not cope with their pain and asked them to be strong for me.

From that moment, my journey became their journey. Their crossroads would be different from mine, but just as painful.

The weeks ahead were difficult, going from doctor to doctor and doing test after test. My coping strategy was to deal only with what each day brought and not think too much about what lay ahead. Christmas was approaching and I tried to focus on organising gifts for my family. I tried to keep our life as normal as possible.

The results of the tests and scans revealed that the cancerous tumour was in my rectum. I would need a week of radiotherapy in the hope of shrinking the tumour before surgery. All was in place for the next step of my journey. I attended Belvoir Park Hospital for further scans, so that they could mark out the areas to be treated. This was to be the moment when the reality of what was happening in my life really set in. As my sister drove us through the hospital gates that morning, I felt real fear for the first time since being given my diagnosis. My sister decided to stay with me throughout rather than just drop me off. Later, when I asked her why she changed her plans, she answered, 'You needed me more.' She had seen my fear.

I was shown into a room with scanners and various other medical devices. This in itself didn't concern me, but as the staff explained what I was about to experience, I felt totally out of control. With no choice in the matter, I simply had to endure what was ahead and, without giving all the finer details of this experience, I was left feeling humiliated. The fact I could not be in control of what was happening to my body was frightening. I closed my eyes and prayed: 'Please God, give me the strength and courage to endure.' I would repeat this prayer many times on my journey.

That week of treatment was emotionally draining for me and I was relieved when my last visit ended. I prayed I would never need to return there, but seeing so many other people going through their own cancer journeys gave me strength – I was not alone. The crossroads once again appeared in front of me, and I asked myself: 'Which road do I take on the next step of my journey?' I chose to stay positive, face the unknown and pray that God would give me the strength and courage that I knew would be needed to face the major surgery scheduled for 16 December 2003.

We all know how hectic preparing for Christmas can be, and I put all my effort into doing just that. Putting up the Christmas tree was always something I enjoyed, so that year I decided this would be the most beautifully decorated tree we had ever had (and it was). Making flower arrangements is one of my hobbies, and I would make Christmas arrangements for family and friends each year. Again, I decided they would all have the best I could make (and they did). It was the first Christmas that I was so well organised!

I surprised myself, but what all this did for me was to keep me occupied with things I enjoyed doing and keep my mind focused. That is not to say I forgot about what lay ahead: how could I? There were moments when I would be overcome with emotion and the fear that I might not survive the surgery. I had decided I was not giving up without a fight, but I did not know then how hard the battle would be.

The night before my admittance to hospital was a very emotional time for all the family. The phone never stopped ringing, visitors kept arriving, and at one stage I felt like screaming: 'Do you all think I am not coming back?' The support I received from family and friends was immeasurable and without it, I would not be where I am today. Yet although this support was needed and I will be forever grateful for it, I also needed time to be on my own. Unless someone experiences personally the effects of a cancer diagnosis, they truly do not understand the impact this has on a person's physical and mental well-being.

My admittance to hospital was straightforward and I surprised myself by being quite calm. The consultant arrived in my room and I knew from his manner that he was a little anxious. After a few moments, he explained that because of the position of my tumour, it would be impossible to rejoin my bowel after the tumour was removed – I was to have a permanent colostomy. The impact of this was not to hit home until much later: all I could think about at the time was getting the tumour out, no matter what it took.

My eyes opened as I was being wheeled back to the ward after the surgery was over – 'I have survived!' The first faces I saw were those of my husband Jack and my children, Jacqueline, Pamela and Jonathan. I remember smiling at them all and their worried faces smiling back. My body was mutilated and changed forever; but I was alive and I was about to start my journey of recovery.

Once back on the ward, the nursing staff were busy round me, sorting out drips, drains and checking on my wounds. I thought, 'My God. What have they done to me?' I seemed to be attached to all sorts. When I was informed that I would need a transfusion of four units of blood, I thought, 'I hope it's good stuff – I surely need it!' Eventually my family were allowed to see me, and I focused on letting them know I was okay. Just seeing them all and being able to talk with them was the best medicine. My next focus was to get home for Christmas. It would be a challenge, but it was an aim I was determined to achieve.

The days following my surgery were difficult, both physically and emotionally. I faced the fact of having the colostomy, but it was too early to be able to accept the change in my body image. I thought that with time, acceptance would come. I tried to keep my spirits up when the stoma nurse was discussing what appliance would be best for me. I had a choice (at last!) of a one-piece or a two-piece. I remember stating that if I was to have a bag, I wanted a designer one, preferably a Gucci! As it happened, they were out of stock, so I made do with the tried and tested one instead.

Three days until Christmas, and my family and I were in the consultant's office hearing the results of my pathology report. My tumour was Stage Two. The consultant and my oncologist were confident that the surgery had been successful in removing all of the tumour and affected tissue, so no chemotherapy was needed. I was so relieved to hear those words, 'No chemo needed'. This had been something I was dreading, as I have a phobia about taking drugs. I had even refused any strong pain relief after the surgery.

On the morning of Christmas Eve, the last drain was removed. Now was my chance for escape: 'I'll be home for Christmas!' When my consultant came to see me on his ward rounds, I asked to go home. He was reluctant to let me go, but I pleaded with him and won. My daughters Jacqueline and Pamela took me home that night, still in my pyjamas. I wouldn't let them go to get my clothes: I just wanted out of hospital and did not care what I wore. The memory of arriving home that Christmas Eve night was and still is the most wonderful feeling of peace and serenity I have ever felt.

Christmas Day had its highs and lows. I laughed as my husband Jack tried to instruct my son-in-law Gary how to do the roast potatoes, when he had no cooking skills himself! It was a pantomime in my kitchen that morning, as three men battled with making dinner. The girls set a beautiful table fit for a queen (me!), and I was seated at the head of the table, facing Jack and with my wonderful family around me. Through the laughter, many thoughts went through my mind, but I did not share them: they were too difficult to explain.

I returned to hospital on Boxing Day as instructed, to have some of my stitches removed. This was unpleasant, as part of my wound had opened. However I wasn't concerned: it was just a small setback, one of many I would face. The district nurse was informed and they called daily with me at home to dress and check the healing. I also had the district stoma nurse call regularly to measure and check the forming of the stoma. Not a pleasant part of the process, but funny at times. I was good at letting the nurses think I was okay with this new waste disposal system they gave me, but I was far from okay with it. I called it many names (I'll leave it to your imagination as to what some of these names might have been!)

My abdominal wound was healing well but I was having problems with the perianal wound. I had developed a fistula and was scheduled for more surgery in February 2004. Again, I found myself in hospital, preparing for theatre.

It was then that I was informed I had contracted the MRSA bug. This had not been disclosed to me before I had been discharged, and I was angry. I don't know what came over me that day, but I suddenly got this fear of going back into theatre. I needed to speak with my consultant. He came to see me and I asked if it was possible for the fistula to heal eventually on its own, without more surgery. The answer was: 'Possibly'. I decided to take that chance. I was taking control and making my own choices again.

Back home without having had the surgery, I faced the daily struggle with pain, fatigue and the constant problems with the waste disposal system. Days turned to weeks and weeks into months, as I tried to find ways to cope with all that was happening. There were many days when the frustration of coping with various symptoms and setbacks left my emotions in turmoil. I had learned to hide my deepest feelings from my family. I simply needed to protect them from the anxiety I felt.

As time passed, I was still dealing with many issues and it was at this point that my GP referred me to the Marie Curie Day Therapy Unit for further support. I remember feeling lost the first day I arrived there – this was somewhere I did not want to be, and I almost turned to leave and go back home as soon as I got there. I realise on reflection, however, that the support I received from the wonderful people I met through Marie Curie and the time I spent there marked a turning point for me. I gained strength and was given invaluable help in learning to manage the chronic fatigue and constant pain I was having to endure daily. The programme of support offered at the Therapy Unit there enabled me to move on with renewed energy and a more positive frame of mind.

June 2004 brought me great sorrow, when my eldest brother Charles died suddenly after a two-week illness (not cancer related). Myself and my remaining brothers and sisters were devastated. We as siblings were always close, and losing Charles strengthened that bond even more. My brother's last words to me were to tell me to be strong and take care of myself. I knew the journey forward would be difficult, but I was determined to do my very best and make each day count.

It was at this point in my journey that my dearest friend Susan became my confidant. I had known Susan as a work colleague for a few years when she worked in Medical Records in Ards Hospital, and I was in Outpatients. Neither of us knew then how our lives would change and how a casual friendship would become a bond that we both would cherish. In August 2003, Susan had been diagnosed with breast cancer and I had supported her through that difficult time, not knowing that three months later I too would be given a cancer diagnosis. As Susan and I continued in our determination to get back to some form of normal life and return to work, we shared our deepest feelings about the physical and emotional scars we had both suffered. It was by doing this that we helped each other find ways of dealing with the losses our cancer diagnoses had brought us. Surprisingly to some, Susan and

I laughed a lot. The laughter at times would come after one of us had shed tears. Quite often we laughed at each other. The continual hospital appointments were ongoing for us both, but together we shared the anxiety and emotional stress that seemed at times to be never-ending.

It was through all this that Susan and I saw at first hand the people who struggled without good support. While attending various clinics, we had the opportunity to meet so many people and hear them talk about their own experiences. This sowed the seed for us, to want to help others get the support they needed and have access to information that would be beneficial to their personal requirements. Although there were a lot of good services for cancer patients, there were still gaps in the system. It was then that we thought of getting a support group started. I wrote letters to various people and organisations that I hoped would help. Some were interested; others wished us good luck with our idea, but could not give us the support to get started. The Chief Executive at the Ulster Hospital at that time suggested that we meet with the Head of Cancer Services to discuss our ideas.

This meeting was to be the starting point for getting the support group off the ground. Susan and I also met with representatives from several cancer charities to put our ideas to them, and eventually our efforts were rewarded. A local cancer charity agreed to facilitate a support group on a trial basis of six months. It was the news Susan and I had prayed for. We decided from the start to have a generic group: no one was to be excluded. There were no other generic groups at this time, but Susan and I had learned from our personal experience that although we each had cancer invade different parts of our bodies, the effects were similar in many ways.

The first meeting of the HOPE (**H**elping **O**thers **P**rogress **E**very day) cancer support group took place at Ards Hospital in 2006. We began with five members, including myself and Susan. Today, almost five years on, the group is going from strength to strength. We have achieved what we had hoped for: offering support to those affected by cancer.

The hand of fate was to strike yet again, however, when Susan was told that her cancer had returned. It was devastating news. The months that followed saw the two of us spend hours in different hospitals, as

Susan went through intensive treatment. Through all this, we still found time for laughter. It was so important to make every day count. At one point Susan had a break in her treatment regime, so together we took off to her brother's seaside caravan. What beautiful memories I have of those precious days we shared. Susan was a great animal lover. She had three dogs: Sheba (a Great Dane), Beauty (a Labrador) and Duke (a Lurcher). They were her babies, and so they too had to come to the caravan. It was a hoot! I had my little dog Jessie: a Shih Tzu and a cheeky madam who bossed the others. The long walks along the shoreline, with the dogs free to run, were great medicine for Susan. I took some great photos. The time we spent there gave us quality time to discuss all we had experienced, but for Susan it was also a chance to talk of her feelings about what she had yet to face.

One of our aims from the beginning had been that one day we both would return to work. For Susan, the realisation that this would never happen for her was another loss she had to experience. But she accepted it, and encouraged me to get back to work as soon as I felt strong enough. Six months later, even though occupational health gave me the go ahead to have a trial period back at work at reduced hours, I was told by Human Resources that they had nothing for me. My working life in a job I loved had been coldly taken away. What fresh challenges was life going to throw my way next? Again, I stood at a crossroads – 'Which road do I take now?' At that moment, I had no idea what to do. I was lost.

Arriving home from a support group meeting one evening, Jack and I were given the wonderful news that we were going to become grandparents. Here was something that the whole family could celebrate! Our grandson, Charlie (named after my brother), was born in May 2006. I was a grandmother. I was present at his birth – words cannot describe how I felt at that moment.

But my joy was soon to turn to tears, when in June 2006, my eldest sister Jean died suddenly. I was there when she fell unconscious, and I worked to resuscitate her, while waiting for the emergency services. Our combined efforts failed and she was gone. Once again, the family were facing the loss of another sibling and once again we drew strength from each other. This was such a difficult time. I felt myself falling into a black pit again – but I knew that if I let that happen, I might never find my way back out. My cancer had not taken me – I was alive. There was a reason for this, and I decided I was going to focus on each day and make it count. Spending time daily with my children and my new grandson helped ease the sorrow I felt. July 2006 was another emotional journey for me, when I sat in the halls of Queen's University and watched as my son Jonathan received his degree in Biological Science. I cried tears of joy. I had thought when I was given my diagnosis that I would not see this day, and I gave thanks to God for this precious moment.

The months ahead were spent with Susan as she battled to survive. I spent every day with her, giving all the support I could. We would sometimes sit outside on her garden swing, not saying a word – just lost in our own thoughts. Then we would laugh, whenever we both went to speak at the same time. I was losing my dearest friend. Many times I drove home with tears streaming down my face. I asked God why, but as we know, there is no answer to such a question.

In August 2007, Susan's battle ended. She died at peace in her own home: a request she had asked her husband to make possible for her. Susan was a remarkable woman who showed great strength and courage throughout her illness, and in her darkest days, she still thought of others and always found time for laughter. What an infectious laugh she had! I can still hear it.

Again, the experience of loss was hard to bear. I was once again standing at a crossroads, not knowing where to turn. I prayed that this roller coaster of emotions I had been on would stop and let me off, even for just a short while. The weeks which followed were emotionally very difficult for me and I found myself reflecting more on what I had experienced in my life. During this period of reflection, I rediscovered that I was a strong person, and I would face the road ahead with a positive mind.

It still surprises me how opportunity can open doors when you least expect it. Information was forwarded to me regarding a course I might be interested in, at the Macmillan Centre next to the City Hospital. I phoned the tutor, to get details of what the work would involve before I asked to be considered for the course. The Cancer Support Certificate was the name of the qualification the course would lead to. It was to cover five modules and would take a year to complete.

I was accepted onto the course, but my first day travelling to the Centre was full of anxiety. I started to doubt myself – my confidence had been kicked about since my diagnosis, and I was feeling scared. 'What if my new waste disposal system breaks down?' My mind was in overdrive. That is when a voice inside me shouted: 'Go for it – you can do it!' And I did. One year later, on graduation day, this time I was proud of *me*. I had completed the course, and what a learning experience it was. Finishing this course was the beginning of rebuilding my confidence, and rebuilding myself. Many times on my cancer journey, feelings of hopelessness would cloud my mind. And it would be at these moments that I would strive to accomplish some small goal – and this would always help to banish the feeling of hopelessness.

I have always been one for reflecting on life, as I believe we all can learn from our experiences. It was from this belief that my vision for a 'Garden of Reflection' took shape. Finding a suitable place for such a garden was made possible with the support of Ards Borough Council, who offered a piece of ground at the Kiltonga Wildlife Sanctuary (the 'Duck Pond') in Newtownards. The members of the HOPE Generic Cancer Support Group and other volunteers worked together to create a peaceful setting there for all to use.

For me, the garden is a special place, and I like to spend time alone there to reflect. I can find comfort and peace of mind in this place, as there is something so calming about just watching and listening to nature there: sights and sounds that so many people simply never take the time to notice. My grandson Charlie – now 4 years old and ready for school – also loves to go to the garden and help me plant things there. He calls it 'Nanny's Special Garden': that is priceless!

I have reached the part of my journey where I have found acceptance of what I experienced. There will be other crossroads and challenges ahead, I know, and I hope and pray God will give me the strength to face them.

Don't let circumstances dictate your life:
Deal powerfully with your circumstances and create your life for
yourself.

The cancer journey is a difficult and emotional one for those who must travel it. I pray that by sharing my personal experience I will have given hope to someone.

(*All extracts and quotations are from *The Irish Get Up and Go Diary 2010*
by Glenda Devlin, Chicco, 2010)

Hope

Hope puts up with modest gains, realising that the longest
journey starts with the first step;
Hope opens doors where despair closes them;
Hope discovers what can be done, instead of grumbling about
what cannot;
Hope lights a candle, instead of cursing the darkness;
Hope pushes ahead when it would be easy to quit;
Hope draws its power from a deep trust in God and the basic
goodness in humankind.

The Puzzle of My Life

I look at my life as a giant puzzle. You feel confident when the pieces fit together and the picture looks promising. Then when you least expect it, the pieces get misplaced and anxiety sets in.

How do you go about getting the picture back? With a positive mind and focus you can regain most of the image you strive for.

Then once again the puzzle looks different; the pieces don't fit the way you hoped they would. Anxiety, stress, emotional turmoil once again threaten you. A piece is lost; it is irreplaceable.

What can you do to fill the empty space? As you try to fill in the missing piece with something positive, you discover there are more pieces lost.

How or why has this happened? You took so much care to ensure that you kept the picture in focus.

The reality is that no matter how well you prepare, and no matter what precautions you put in place, something or someone will change the image you had hoped for.

Move forward with a positive focus and the puzzle will have a final image. Each piece of it will hold a story that is yours. Look at the puzzle many times and reflect what joy it brought and what blessings it rewarded you with, and thank God for them. Be grateful that the time spent putting the image together will have lasting memories, not only for you but for others.

The final piece will not be placed by you as there is only one other person who has the power to put it in its resting place. As I don't know when the final piece will appear, I will continue to work on the image I hope for. I will search out the brightest pieces around and focus on placing them in the puzzle.

Kathy Cash
Bowel Cancer, 2003

Perseverance

Christine Hunt
Breast Cancer, 2004 and 2008

Perseverance

When trials intrude to slow down your life,
It would be easy for you to give in,
But by perseverance you'll overcome strife,
So just keep plodding on.

Christine Hunt
Breast Cancer, 2004 and 2008

KEEP LOOKING UP!

Billy
Bowel Cancer, 2008

Symptoms and First Signs

I had had occasional trouble with piles now and again in the past, but towards the end of 2008, this bleeding was a little bit worrying. After about three weeks, when it hadn't gone away, I reckoned that a visit to the doctor was unavoidable, so off I went to see my GP. She was absolutely amazing. I had realised that this was potentially a serious complaint and my GP shared my fears: 'raising the red flag' was how she described it, I think, and she felt it necessary to refer me to see a consultant. Not what I wanted to hear, but her reaction confirmed my fears that this could well be cancer. I was convinced in fact that it almost certainly was.

Coping with Fear

The first person to share with was, of course, my wife, but that evening after my visit to the GP, I also phoned two of my friends. Not the sort of thing that men are inclined to do, but for me it just didn't seem to be a problem. I'd been a Christian for 34 years, but that did not mean I was immune from fear or anxiety. Cut me and I do bleed, just like the next man.

So I didn't hesitate in phoning these guys, telling them that I had a potentially serious medical complaint and that I would really appreciate their prayers and those of their wives. They were both listening hard and I knew that I could really depend upon them – all four! While on the phone, one of the guys encouraged me to read Psalm 100 and immediately our conversation ended, I turned to the prescribed passage. There are just five verses in the Psalm, but on this occasion I only got as far as verse 3: 'He (God) hath created us, and we are His.' Upon reading these words I seemed to be stopped in my tracks by God saying to me, 'What more do you need?' I can honestly say that my fears of cancer were swallowed up by the knowledge that as a Christian, I belonged to the God of all creation.

For some time afterwards, I quietly thought of the blessing contained in these words of encouragement, and they really did help me to focus on God and my relationship with Him. At no stage was I thinking along the lines that I would be suddenly healed and free of this disease, but very simply, I was being reassured that I was absolutely safe, because of my relationship with God in Jesus. One of the expressions often used among the 'cancer fraternity' is that as a patient you are 'on a journey', and as far as I was concerned, I was much reassured that I was not on my own on this journey. Not only did I have the solid support of family and friends, but I also had the God of all creation with me along the way.

Appointments

A series of appointments were to follow and the time really did seem to drag at first. My second appointment, about 4 weeks after visiting my GP, was for a camera check of the bowel, and on this occasion they also took a biopsy. Some days later, this sample was confirmed as testing positive (i.e. showing cancer cells), and another appointment quickly followed, for me to have the growth – or 'polyps' – removed. Soon afterwards, I was to have a CAT scan and then an MRI scan.

And then it was time for the consultation! The surgeon was very honest and clearly explained the position that I was in. They could not be certain that by removing the polyps they had removed all traces of cancer. In addition to this, the scans showed up two areas of irregularity outside the bowel. These could well have been irritation from the procedure to remove the polyps, the surgeon explained, but could also indicate something more sinister. Only surgery could positively say what was really happening, and indeed surgery was the consultant's professional recommendation. He said they were reasonably confident that my condition had been detected early enough and was therefore treatable. Now that was music to my ears! Well, I wasn't exactly dancing, but without hesitation I asked that they go ahead and plan the surgery. My poor wife was numb with all that she was hearing, but I had already rehearsed the possible scenarios in my own mind, and was well prepared in advance.

Support

It is absolutely amazing what can materialise at a time of great need. Several cancer patients made contact with me to give advice and encouragement. Some had made good recoveries, and others were still at various stages of going through treatment. All of these folks made it their business to pass on what they could, so that my journey might be just a little bit easier. People can be so kind and caring and there were times when all the expressions of genuine concern were quite overwhelming. With many of these folks, I built up a genuine friendship and I can only hope that I was able to encourage them too.

A 'No-No' Question

People usually mean well, but sometimes they can say the wrong thing. The one question I could not abide was: 'What's the prognosis?' Now, I perfectly understand that when someone is diagnosed as having cancer, instinctively we wonder just how serious it might be for that individual. But I would strongly suggest that this question regarding prognosis should *never* be directed at the patient themselves. On the couple of occasions when I was asked this question, I speedily replied: 'The prognosis is, I am planning to live. I am not actually planning to die.'

I really do feel that this is a 'no-no' question, as it is just a bit too personal. A patient may well want to share this prognosis thing with certain people at a certain time. But this decision and its timing are for the patient to determine and no one else. Indeed, some patients don't even want to know anything themselves regarding the prognosis. So, a little bit of thought, please, before you ask.

Surgery

Just ten days before Christmas 2008, and I was going under the knife. As part of the preparation for this, I had had five days of radiotherapy. This procedure itself was a doddle, compared to some of the other things to follow, and of course the staff were superb in explaining the process and giving reassurance. This also afforded me my first exposure to other cancer patients undergoing treatment of some kind. The waiting area in the hospital was an education for me. So many people of varying ages, and all of them requiring treatment for cancer.

The radiotherapy was short-lived and immediately followed by the surgery. I would have a 'bag' afterwards and this was all going to be very new territory. If the stoma appeared on my right side, then it would be temporary and reversible. On the left, and it would be a permanent fixture. The surgeon could not be certain in advance of the operation, and so I would only learn the outcome on the other side.

Preparation for the surgery was extremely professional. Pre-surgery appointments, the prep itself, counselling from specialist nursing staff from various disciplines: all this made it so much more reassuring. I was ok about this surgery and still very much in my thinking were the words of the Psalmist: 'He hath created us, and we are His'.

The Other Side

It was on the right. Yesss!! No, I didn't jump up and down with excitement, but the words 'temporary and reversible' were so good to think upon. I was so thankful to God. I spent another five days in hospital following surgery and that was quite an experience in itself. We even managed a bit of humour as part of the experience and, believe me, a bit of humour does go a long way. Dignity was certainly out of the window, but I have to say that the nursing staff were great in jollying me along.

Lab Results

About ten days following surgery, I had an appointment with a specialist colorectal nurse in the hospital. My surgeon, having just received the lab results and knowing of my appointment, came to see me while I was there. Again and again, he was going the extra mile. He is a very special and caring person!

The procedure to remove the polyps had in fact been very successful, in that there were no further traces of cancer in the surrounding tissue. From that perspective, the major bowel surgery I had might not have been necessary. However, the two areas of irregularity that had shown up on the scans were in fact four tumours. Now, that certainly made the surgery worthwhile. Furthermore, because of where the tumours were and the seriousness of the cancer, it was deemed necessary that I should have chemotherapy as well. This would affect the timetable for reversal of the 'bag', as such a procedure would have to wait until I had completed six months of chemo. This was a small inconvenience really, and I certainly was not complaining. The surgery had been deemed successful in removing all the tumours, and this chemotherapy was to mop up any cancer cells that might still be lurking about.

Recovery Time

Following surgery I was given about eight weeks to recover before the commencement of chemo. It was a time for healing, but also a time of serious adjustment to my circumstances. How would I cope with a 'bag'? I had tried not to think too far ahead, but essentially trusted the counsel and recommendations of the health professionals. This formula seemed to work for me, and coping with the 'bag' was not a terrifying experience, I found.

I've never had a good stomach for strong odours, or anything with the potential of an odour even. I'm the wimp that leaves the room when nappies are being changed – even if they're only wet ones! But, explain it as you may, I can honestly look back and say that I adapted to coping with the 'bag' really well. I reasoned that I had no choice, other than to get on with it.

Blessed with a house full of women, I never thought the day would arrive when I would take over the bathroom. Managing the bag did not take all that long, really, but I suppose the full package of getting sorted in the mornings did take me about forty-five minutes. It was quite a ritual, though I soon got used to it. Now, we are all different when it comes to our plumbing, or the workings of it. Mine was such that I found I had to visit the toilet a couple of times every night. To manage this safely I would in fact set my alarm for an interval of three-and-a-half hours at a time. So sleep was enjoyed in instalments of just three-and-a-half hours. This became routine though, and my body seemed to cope with it ok.

Chemotherapy

Just two months after surgery, my follow-up treatment was to commence. I hadn't realised there were so many cocktails of chemo, but I was to learn fast. Following chats with my surgeon, specialist nurses and former patients, I was convinced that the cocktail I was to be given would be really quite mild and very manageable. So you can imagine how surprised I was when the oncologist who explained the treatment to me outlined a regime that seemed just a bit too severe. I tried to correct him of course (as one does!), thinking that perhaps he had been reading someone else's file and had got it totally wrong. 'No,' he said. 'You have a more serious form of cancer and we will have to treat you with a more rigorous course of treatment.' That certainly took the wind out of my sails, but I had to bow to his professional judgement and expertise.

I was scheduled for eight treatments over a 24 week period, consisting of a two-hour infusion, followed by chemo in tablet form for fourteen days. About one hour into the first infusion, I started to experience pain in the arm that was taking the drugs and the staff had to finish the infusion in my other arm. Well, I did mention that I was something of a wimp! My vein simply could not cope with the toxic mix that was passing through it. It was then recommended that I should have a PICC line inserted for further treatments, and that would be there for the duration of my treatments.

Back to the first treatment session, though. Infusion completed, I headed home with a chemist's shop in my rucksack. It was probably the tablet form of chemo, but man, was I sick. Sick as a parrot, in fact! Doctors and nursing staff did their best to stabilise me with anti-sickness medication, but after five days of taking the tablets, I was advised to abort. My regime was changed to a lesser dosage of the same cocktail, but all in liquid form and every two weeks instead of every three. Also, it would now be twelve treatments instead of eight, so essentially I was getting the same cocktail of treatment as originally prescribed, only in a more manageable form that my body could perhaps better cope with.

I continued to be quite sick over the next few months of treatment, but the doctors in the treatment unit adjusted my cocktail of drugs so that I would manage as best as possible. Reading this, you might well think that chemotherapy is an altogether scary prospect. While it is certainly not to be desired, I would want to say that it should not be feared. Many other patients receive the same cocktail as I was given, without being sick. But most important to note is the support and professionalism of the nursing staff and doctors in the Treatment Unit. They did not want to make my life miserable and made every effort to keep things on track for me.

Vulnerability and Exploitation

Being faced with cancer does leave a person pretty vulnerable. It certainly means being confronted with the possibility of death, and that will often leave a person open to exploitation by any quack or guru who comes along with a magic formula. Again and again, fellow patients have told me that they would try anything – and who could fault them for that? But cancer patients don't need any further pain in their lives, and to be given false hope from any source is particularly cruel. Now I would not say that every alternative to standard treatments is 'off the rails' and should be avoided. But great care needs to be taken, and when 'alternatives' are mooted, support and advice from family and friends can indeed be priceless.

Sitting in a waiting room at the Treatment Unit afforded me opportunity to meet lots of fellow patients. Never once did I ask anyone anything regarding their type of cancer or prognosis, but in practically every instance, I was privileged to listen, as patients shared their most personal experiences of having cancer. Looking back now on those days in the Treatment Unit, I have concluded that, above all, most patients need someone to listen. Not to interrogate or pontificate or preach, but simply to listen and show a genuine interest in the whole person. For me, some of those meetings in the Treatment Unit were the start of solid friendships. Some of these friends are, sadly, no longer with us, but others are still going strong to this day.

'Never trivialise what you are going through'

Following my week of radiotherapy, pre-surgery, I mentioned to a specialist nurse one day that seeing all those patients with perhaps even more serious cancer than myself – and many of them so much younger than I was – had helped me put things in perspective. To this, the nurse replied, 'Never trivialise what you yourself are going through. Yes, what those patients are going through is difficult and traumatic for them. But what you are going through is every bit as difficult and traumatic for you.' She spoke a lot of sense, and I didn't forget what she said. In fact, there have been several occasions on which I have quoted her advice to fellow patients who I felt needed a bit of steering.

Moving On

It is just over a year since my last treatment, and I am so very thankful for the good health that I have. No traces of cancer. There are some side-effects from the treatment that will probably be permanent, but nothing that cannot be managed. Some restriction of movement from the surgery too, but this is manageable too, and getting better.

I nearly forgot to mention the 'reversal' surgery. This meant six days in hospital – but now, almost one year on from that, I am still jumping up and down.

'He has created us, and we are His'

My experience of this journey has very much been a spiritual one, of becoming more aware of my utter dependence upon God and feeling absolutely secure in the knowledge that I belong to Him. If I have been able to think positively, it has been in my belief that God loves me and cares for me. I am still looking up!

Psalm 121: 1-2: 'I lift up my eyes to the hills – where does my help come from? My help comes from the Lord, the Maker of heaven and earth.'

Billy
Bowel Cancer, 2008

45

Pauline's Story

Pauline Hamilton
Ovarian Cancer, 2009

Ouch!

Monday, 11 May 2009

Today, I feel totally fed up and pissed off! I'm just back from the doctor's, having had an unpleasant weekend. Guess what – anti-arthritic drugs have possibly caused bleeding in my stomach, and I have to stop all meds and go on an antacid for a month. *So* not funny. We did tell the consultant (by we, I mean me and GP) that my stomach was very sensitive and had bled before, after I had taken a Beechams powders.

So he had just prescribed a stomach tablet as well as the anti-arthritic drugs and said all would be fine. Well, it's not fine – I am in a lot of pain because of this. We are supposed to put our trust in bloody doctors. What for?

Sorry – *so* pissed off and fed up. And sore.

Huge Shock Today!

Tuesday, 12 May 2009

So, to continue from yesterday, I had an appointment with my rheumatologist this afternoon. I had a lot more pain today and the drive to the hospital (the Ulster Clinic) was dreadful. Anyway, when I got there, I was a mess and my doctor asked me what had happened and then asked me to lie down while he examined me. I didn't want him to touch my stomach, as it was so sore. He was gentle enough and then said he would be back in a minute. Next thing I know, I am getting whisked away for X-rays, followed by an ultrasound and then a CT scan. I was *so* frightened and because I wasn't expecting this, I was there alone.

So, all tests were done, while I cried and screamed like a baby (I was totally hysterical!) – and now I have the results. . . I have multiple cysts on my ovaries, so large they are pushing my stomach up, hence the pain. I certainly wasn't expecting that. I thought 'Rheumy' was going to give me a bloody Milk of Magnesia or something. And now this. And there was me, ready yesterday for telling him off. Now it seems that my GP has missed a large problem. So now which doctors do I believe in?

Bigger Shock – Kidnapping!
Day One of my Captivity
Wednesday, 13 May 2009

I managed to go into work today, to take my mind off things. I have just had a call from my GP: the Ulster Clinic has rung. My scans have been reviewed overnight and I have a blood clot on my leg now. Yet more hysterics. People in work all trying to keep me calm. *Calm? I am petrified!*

They won't let me drive, or let anyone else drive me. I am waiting for an ambulance to take me to hospital.

Ambulance arrived, I walked outside. The paramedics ran behind me with a wheelchair – yeah, right! I am *so* not getting in a wheelchair! The ambulance was very hot, I was hysterical again and I just wanted to open the door and jump out. They had turned the heating up, as I had turned pale and clammy – from fear! I got to the Ulster Hospital and they *made* me sit in a wheelchair. I was mortified! I tried to tell them I was ok, but they wouldn't listen and put me into a 'holding bay'. Several times over the next eight hours, I was told they might let me go home again. Several times, I was told that no, I had to stay and they would eventually find a bed for me. At 3.10 a.m., I got a bed on Ward 15 – after someone died there. *Lovely!*

Day Two of my Captivity
Thursday, 14 May 2009

Still in hospital, getting Heparin injections to treat the clot. They won't let me move, I'm even wheeled to go for a pee! I'm bored and typing this on a hand-held keypad. Feeling ok, but don't want to be here.

Day Four of my Captivity
Saturday, 16 May 2009

They have moved me to Gynae ward, as my ovaries are 'of major concern'. What the hell does that mean anyway?

The blood clot is actually in my groin and not my leg, which is why I am confined to bed. But they don't understand why my leg isn't swollen, so have ordered a second ultrasound which will be on Monday. They can't give me Warfarin in case an op is required soon, so I will be here for a while. The girls in work sent me a 'Doctors Pulling Kit', complete with fishnet stockings, which I sexily wore over my hospital anti-clot stockings! At least it gave people a laugh.

I'm not in pain, just bored and s**t-scared.

Day Eight of my Captivity
Wednesday, 20 May 2009

I was moved to the City Hospital today. I wanted to go to the Ulster Clinic but was told I need quite a specialist operation, so the City it was. The whole way there I was asking the paramedics what Ward Four in the City was – if it was a Cancer ward, I wasn't going!

Blood clot(s) is/are because of the weight of a tumour in my pelvis, don't know if benign or not. Have been allowed out of bed today, seeing Vascular and Gynae tomorrow.

I'm very frightened but still trying to laugh. So far all doctors concerned have been good-looking, which helps a bit – some pleasant scenery! Is this a pattern with Gynae doctors? Is this concerning? Oh, I don't really care – it helps pass the day.

Day Twelve of my Captivity
Sunday, 24 May 2009

Well guys, I didn't have a good night: I am scared. Scared of what has happened, scared of what is going to happen, scared of what they will find, scared for my future.

As I lie in my hospital bed, all I see are posters about ovarian cancer staring me in the face. Ovarian cancer – the so-called silent killer. Will I be lucky and have a low-grade cancer and my op to remove it all will be sufficient, or . . . Well, I don't have to spell it out.

This is s**t, talk about knockbacks. Yes, I am feeling sorry for myself today. I am not feeling positive, and I hate this. I am not in pain, but mentally I feel overwhelmed.

God, I just want a hug – and someone to tell me everything will be ok.

Day Thirteen of my Captivity
Sunday, 24 May 2009

Hoorah! They let me go home today, on day release. *At last* – freedom!

I had a lot of things to do: pay the bills, check the cats were ok (neighbour kindly feeding them), and so on. It was also good to lie in my own bath. They made me promise I would come back, so I asked if they wanted me to wear an ankle strap!!

I felt a lot happier, making sure my bills were paid and all was ok. I also managed to go to the shops and buy a few things for the ward – biscuits, chocolate, magazines, etc.

Day Fifteen of my Captivity
Wednesday, May 27 2009

Naff all to update, still here. Bored, tired and grumpy! They aren't doing the filter procedure until Friday morning, before the big op in the p.m. It's a conspiracy to keep me here!

Day Twenty of my Captivity
Monday, 1 June 2009

I'm still here!

Big op over – 48 staples in my abdomen. I think my modelling days are over!

All signs of tumour have been removed, but it will take 8-10 days for the results . . . S**t!

I remember very little about the last 48 hours, really – except that the pain was bad all weekend, like severe acid pain at the top of my stomach. I complained about this but was told by the duty anaesthetist that I was ok. So I then spent Sunday night throwing up. Talk about being scared! I was holding on to my staples, having visions of them hitting the far wall every time I retched. *Not* good!

I hope I am turning a corner now – I should be home by next Sunday. They didn't fit the vena cava filter after all. Apparently, my body broke down the clot all by itself (I'm just *such* a clever chick!). The radiologist just worked away and didn't talk to me. I got scared and I asked him to tell me what was happening – nothing. I ended up screaming for someone to tell me what was going on! Luckily, nursing staff came to my rescue and kept me calm. I hope I never have to see that radiologist again! Wouldn't be *so* much easier if people like this at least talked to their patients?

A Positive Story
Friday, 5th June 2009

I'm going home – *so* happy, after 24 long days and nights in captivity!

My last night in hospital, thank God. I made the nurse put up an EDD on the wall behind me – **E**xpected **D**ate of **D**ischarge, like the ones I had seen above so many other people's beds while I have been stuck in here.

Monday, 8 June 2009

Ok, so now I am back home, feeling quite good, considering the huge op. Obviously have to rest a lot though and won't be back to work for at least another 6 weeks. I'm now on Warfarin for the clot and my bloods are being monitored daily – I *think* this will be for about six months.

I will go back to my consultant on 19 June, when I'll find out the results of my biopsy. I am remaining upbeat and have some peace of mind in the fact that everything has been removed. Something I checked several times with the surgeon . . . lol.

Feeling good!
Friday, June 12 2009

Well, it's now been a week since I was discharged from hospital and I am feeling good. I have very little pain and, although I can't do very much, I am coping well.

My insides do feel different, though. It's a bit strange really, but if I lie down, I have a flat stomach – haven't had that in years, lol. I had lost 21 lbs when I was weighed last, before the op, but I am too scared to get on the scales again. I don't want to believe that some of that may have gone back on due to inactivity! My wound is scabbing up nicely, but it's *so* hard not to pick at the scabs . . . *Gross*, I know!

A district nurse comes out every day to take my bloods to check my

INR level (by which they can measure how long it takes my blood to clot), and then will ring me back later and tell me how many mgs of Warfarin I have to take that day. The only thing I can feel re. the clot(s) is a tingling in my legs. Not quite pins and needles – again, it's a weird feeling, but no pain. Not so sure about this Warfarin malarkey though, all seems to take a lot of everyone's time!

So, all in all, I am doing well. I *so* cannot see me sitting here for another 5 weeks, and I am thinking of going back to work early in July, pending GP approval. It's too boring, sitting here watching crap daytime TV. It's so bad! I have a desk job, so as long as I can get a lift to and from work, I don't see any issue. Maybe I can go back part-time for a week to start off with.

I am still trying to remain positive regarding my histology report next Friday. Yes, I am worried and I have a cry every now and again about it, but that's natural, isn't it?

Ovarian Cancer Confirmed
Monday, 13 June 2009

Well, it's been confirmed: I have ovarian cancer. It's not a shock, but still frightening nonetheless. I have had a good cry, made a few phone calls and for the moment feel okay. I am *sure* I am going to have a lot of wobbles over the next few weeks and months – but for now, I'm calm.

I feel like this past two years, it's just been one thing after the other for me. First, an abusive relationship, followed by meltdown, followed by the arthritis diagnosis, followed now by ovarian cancer. It seems unfair . . .

I have my appointment with the consultant this Friday. I'm numb, just numb . . .

Ok – and the News is?
Friday, 19 June 2009

Ok. So it is Stage 1c Ovarian Cancer, Clear Cell type, and was caused by endometriosis gone bad! I have an 80 per cent chance of complete cure. Hey, those odds are fecking good!

I have my first appointment with the Oncologist on Tuesday 23 June and my chemo will commence a week or so after that. I will need six treatments as a day patient, once every 3 weeks, pending on blood counts being good, etc.

I am feeling ok, I really am. I know my prognosis is good – hell, it could have been a lot worse! I am also going for gene testing, as my mother died from breast cancer. If it is genetic, that makes my chances of recovery even better, they say. And yes, my hair *will* fall out, so I just hope I have a nice-shaped head, lol.

Anyway, folks, that's it. I am sure I will feel sad and teary every now again, but for now I am just glad the prognosis is so good.

Wobble
Sunday, 21 June 2009

Well, I had my first wobble last night. Not a huge surprise, but it kind of came out of the blue. I now realise just how alone I am with this. I so wanted someone to just cuddle me or hold me last night, to let me cry and talk s**t . . . Someone to just be here. I found it very frightening – how the *hell* am I going to get through the next 20 weeks alone in the house? It is going to be so scary, and I'm not sure what I can do.

I looked at wigs online yesterday. Wasn't too upsetting (apart from the price!), though not a huge selection in the style or length I want. Jesus . . . what do I do? Cancer. *I have cancer* . . . So many questions yet unanswered, so many trials yet to come, so much fear and uncertainty: this is just s**t.

Today's Actions, lol
Monday, 22 June 2009

So, today I did a few things. First off, I had a nice bath and got myself ready to go out to the shops. I drove there, but it's only about a mile, so it was fine, no probs at all. Independence, yee haa!

Secondly, I walked into the hairdresser's at the shopping centre, and asked her to take 4 inches off my hair. She did – it's ok and I am ok. I don't suit short hair, but I now have it cut to just below my chin. The hairdresser advised another cut in a few weeks, to take it shorter again, just so my hair loss after chemo won't be such a shock.

I'm glad I made these decisions today. I feel good and now there is no excuse for me not to go to work for a while this week!

Back to Work!
Wednesday, 24 June 2009

So, today – this afternoon – I am going back to work, 3 weeks and 4 days after surgery. To hell with this six weeks' lark, lol. I feel fine: it's a desk job and in a way, I guess I also want to get back to normality. I am due to start chemo this Monday or the next (I don't know yet), and as it's every 3 weeks, I can't just sit around waiting to know if I am going to feel ill or not. They can't tell how anyone reacts to chemo: I might be quite ill, or I might be fine. So, I will suck it and see, lol.

So can't wait to get back to my desk. I'm a happy bunny!

Good News/Bad News!
Monday, 29 June 2009

Ok, so today I went for my pre-chemo appointment and I had two shocks . . . The first was that I have put on seven pounds since I left hospital! Bloody hell, really stop buying those big tubs of Ben & Jerry's ice cream, lol.

The second shock was that I am Stage 1a, not 1c, as I was told by my surgeon 10 days ago! Allegedly, the cancer was in my left ovary only, and had not spread to the right ovary and beyond, as would be the case at Stage 1c. A stomach wash hadn't been done (to check the fluid in the abdomen for cancer cells too), and so it had just been assumed that the cancer was more widespread. While this was of course good news, I had been left for ten days in the belief that my prognosis was worse than it was, with all the worry and heartache that involves! I am angry at that, as the difference between 'a' and 'c' are a lot, especially to me personally. I will be asking more questions about this.

They took bloods in preparation for my chemo, which I will start tomorrow. I'll also get my wig tomorrow – only just found out we get them free while on treatment . . . that's better! I'm a bit scared but still feeling strong and optimistic. I will be fine, just fine!

Tuesday, 30 June 2009

So, here I am at the City Hospital for my first chemo session, nervous but wanting to get this started. It was a little daunting, but I laughed and joked with the nurses who appear relaxed and are easy to chat to.

My first question was, details: 'I need details – please tell me what you are doing and why, every step of the way!' They are obviously used to such a reaction and said, 'No worries, we will do that.'

They put a drip in my left wrist and started giving me the medications I needed. Oh no, it's not just chemo! J First they check the drip is working, with saline, then they give you an anti-sickness drip (for obvious reasons!), antihistamine to prevent allergic reactions, then steroids to try and keep you awake and give you a bit more strength. Then more saline and . . . *then* the chemo started. I asked the nurse to sit with me for a few minutes, as I was scared of the first lot of chemo (in my case Paclitaxel). This wasn't a bother to the nurse, and after a few minutes I was fine. I had a TV to watch and I did so, before spending most of the day dozing on and off. They give you lunch: I was always there on a Tuesday, and every time I was there, I had potato and leek soup with either ham or egg or wilted lettuce salad sandwiches!! I can still smell leek and potato soup! Oh and we got yoghurt and a banana or apple too. And in the middle of all this, I got my wig. I thought it looked good and I was happy.

After three hours, and another flush through with saline, I got the second chemo dose (Carboplatin), which only took 30 minutes. I didn't have any problem while being given the chemo. For me, there is no pain involved in getting chemo but it was a very long day indeed, which left me exhausted.

You get three days' supply of anti-sickness tablets and steroids to take home with you, which I found helped. A lesson I learned very early was take your steroids before 4.00 p.m. – or you will be awake most of the night. Which I was! I could have got up and hoovered the whole house the night after my first chemo treatment, lol!

I Feel Great!

Friday, 3 July 2009

Just a quick update, folks. The chemo was ok. I'm a little bit tired but apart from that, no obvious side effects – yet! I have been back at work full-time all week and I have loved it. I do rest up at night, though: lie on the sofa after dinner, watch a bit of telly, etc. It seems to be working out fine.

I have my second appointment for chemo on 20 July. They are doing it all in one day now, rather than in a day and a half, so that's a lot easier for me for work and for lifts (they won't let me drive when I'm getting chemo).

I have an appointment with my hairdresser tomorrow, so she can style my wig, in preparation for when I need it. I am still undecided as to whether I should wait and see what happens, or just get my hair cut very short now and wear the wig. Decisions, decisions, lol.

So, all in all, it's good . . .

A Bit Run-Down
Friday, 10 July 2009

So, it's now Week Two after chemo, Part One. I feel ok, but this is the week that my immune system gets wiped out, so I am not feeling 100 per cent. This is to be expected!

I had to go to my GP yesterday, to give a urine sample and get bloods taken. I had noticeable blood in my urine, so we think it may be a bladder infection. I have a little pain but nothing too bad. This morning, I woke up and felt exhausted, wiped out and had a bit of a sore throat, so I have not gone into work today. I have Monday and Tuesday off anyway, so I'm glad of that!

The nurses on the 24-hour helpline in my Oncology department are fantastic: I really can't praise them enough. I had to ring them on Sunday as I was having trouble getting my Heparin injections from a chemist. I had tried four different ones and I had rung the on-call GP – his suggestion was to go to Casualty to get the injections done. What?? Useless ass! Oncology were able to source the injections for me from a duty chemist in Bangor. I then had to ring them again on Wednesday, regarding the blood in my urine. They spoke to a doctor and came back to me quickly to tell me to go to GP – and also to reassure me. They rang me yesterday to check I was ok and they will be ringing me again today. It's a great comfort to know that someone is on the other end of the phone when I need them, especially as I live alone.

So, I'm ok folks, feeling under par is only to be expected. Hell, I think I have been very lucky . . . so far!

Oh Gawd!!
Monday, 13 July 2009

Well, this is it: my hair is starting to fall out, two weeks after the first chemo session, as predicted. I'm not sure how I feel, except that I have cried and felt sorry for myself. It's weird – my hair doesn't even hurt if you pull it: it just kind of slips out.

I know I have my wig and I have it cut nicely. And I have just bought several headscarves and bandanas online – longer ones, shorter ones, plain ones and patterned. Hey, guess I have a huge selection, actually, lol.

My bro and sis-in-law are away on hols until next Sunday, and it's a Public Holiday here today – everyone is out watching the parades. And I'm sitting here crying. *How pathetic is that*!

Y'all know me, I will get over this temporary blip. But right now, I'm going to cry . . .

Update
Sunday, 26 July 2009

So here we are, another week over and I am still doing well. I keep telling myself that my next chemo treatment means I'm halfway there. Feels so weird!

As well as chemo this week, I have also had a mammogram, which came back clear (thank God!), and a CT scan. The scan will just be used as a marker, so if my CA125 should come back raised at some point in the future, they will do another scan and compare. I am not planning for that to happen though, lol.

My hair has continued to come out and even though I had it cut to a number 4 two weeks ago, it is causing me a few issues and it's all patchy. I don't know what's worse: my cats shedding their fur all over the house, or me, lol. On Friday night, my head actually hurt as I was in bed – it was like pinpricks all over my head and I couldn't stop it, no matter what way

I lay. So, today I plan to get rid of the rest of it. I will wash my hair (what's left of it) and get rid of as much as I can by rubbing and washing, and then shave off the rest. My eyebrows and eyelashes are still there, and so far when wearing my wig or bandanas, I look normal. Well what passes for normal, anyway, lol.

Apart from that, I am still at work, although a bit tired in the evenings. I really believe work has kept me sane these past weeks. It gives me something else to focus on and keeps my mind occupied. I still go to bed and wake up thinking 'cancer', but isn't that normal? Of course it is! When I wake up, even at the weekend, I don't lie for too long: I get up and *do* something. Another thing, by the way: the steroids sure make you hungry. I like food and lots of it – not huge meals, just grazing all day, nyum nyum!

I am still injecting my Heparin every day too for the blood clot, so my stomach is black/blue/green/purple – and, with my huge scar, boy, I'm attractive right now! With me *not* being a size 10, I actually look like I have an arse on my stomach – no, really! Maybe it's as well that I'm single at the moment . . .

So there ya go, folks . . . Update no. 36 complete, lol.

Halfway There
Monday, 10 August 2009

Had chemo session number 3 today: now halfway through treatment! I am still tired but no other side effects. I am *such* a lucky chick, I really am. I had a bit of a scare this weekend though, as I noticed my abdomen was getting very large again. And of course, I got frightened, thinking the Ascites (OVCA Fluid) had built up again. Today I was told it hadn't, that they wouldn't expect anyone with a normal CA125 to have Ascites. They had a look about and said that this swelling was due to the steroids, which have also caused the swelling on my hands, which has now meant me taking off my rings. It took a lot of effort to get them off today, but we finally managed, with much patience and persuasion!

My CT scan on 22 July was clear: no sign of tumours, no signs of blood clots in my groin – but I still have to continue my injections until I am finished chemo, i.e. the end of October. My CA125 tumour marker is now down to 15. All great and positive news!

There were two people there today who suffered reactions to the chemo (same chemo as mine!). It's basically like anaphylactic shock – you can't breathe, have a tight chest, and so on. They are *so* quick at treating it with steroids and antihistamines but, boy, it is scary to watch. Even scarier for the patients themselves, I'm sure!

In between getting my bloods taken and starting treatment, I usually have about two hours to spare, so today I took myself down to the Macmillan Cancer Support Service (right beside the hospital), to see what goes on there. So, I have booked myself in for Reflexology (which I know I will enjoy) and a bit of counselling: nothing heavy, just informal chats so I can talk things through with people when I need to.

On the Countdown
Friday, 28 August 2009

So, I had chemo session number four today, seeing as Monday is a holiday here. All is good, but I have had a bit of an emotionally traumatic time since my last update.

After my chemo on Monday 10 August, my big bro was taken into the Ulster Hospital that night. He had had a very bad back for several weeks and had been off work. He was kept in overnight and released the following afternoon, with a letter to attend for an MRI scan a few weeks later. He was taken back in on Tuesday night however, after he suddenly felt numb from the waist down. Again, he was kept in hospital overnight and had his MRI scan on the Wednesday at about lunchtime. The results showed a massive prolapsed disc which was blocking every disc below it, hence the numbness. He was sent to the Royal at teatime and operated on that night as, if untreated, he could have been left paralysed. I only have my brother left (my parents died over 20 years ago), so we are very close.

I dashed to the hospital straight from work, so I could see him before he went for surgery – and I did, thank God. I stayed at the hospital with my sister-in-law to keep her company for a while, but I really had to go home at about 11.30 p.m., as I was exhausted. I went in to work a bit later the next morning (Thursday), and then I started bleeding (vaginally). It wasn't too bad and I stayed in work and kept an eye on it.

So, when I got home from work, I was getting myself organised before ringing my Oncology Team, to tell them about the bleeding, when my phone rang. It was my ex-arse! Sorry, but the amount of trouble that man has caused me over the last three years has been just dreadful. I fully believe that stress has been a major contributor to my health going downhill, as my health file prior to 2007 read: measles, 1968; German measles, 1969; psoriasis, 1990 – that was it! *He* was the last person I needed to hear from there and then, and yes, I *should* have put the phone down. But I didn't – one of these days I will learn!

Now, the update on all this is, I went to GP on the Friday (as advised by Oncology) and my bloods were a bit low. I was shaking a lot and they said I was just exhausted and too much had happened over the last few days. I got a week's supply of sleeping pills to get me back on course and I was told to rest, rest and rest again, which I did over the weekend and was fine to go back to work on the Monday. However I got a lot of lower leg pain from the Friday to the Monday, which made it difficult to sleep. I didn't like it, lol!

My brother's surgery was successful and he got home on the Sunday and is recuperating nicely for six weeks. I am so glad he is ok, I really am, and I do love him *so* much.

So, my chemo today was good. My bloods were great, despite getting treatment three days early. I had worked hard on that and ate and drank all the right things – like liver, green leafy veg, lots of fruit (ok, with cream!) and plenty of fluids, etc. The lower leg pain was allegedly caused by stopping the steroids quickly. Re. antihistamines, I was given two options – either to take Paracetamol/Tramadol for a few days, or to take more steroids and cut them down gradually. I have opted for Paracetamol, to see how I go.

Apart from that, the consultant and I are pleased with how everything is going and I have had the go ahead to fly. So I am now looking forward to booking a flight to see my bestest friends in the whole wide world (who live in Spain), a few days after my last treatment in October. That will really give me something to look forward to!

So there ya go, chicks . . . That was a long one, I'm now totally exhausted, lol!

Chemo Number Five!

Tuesday, 21 September 2009

So much for taking some Paracetamol for the leg pains! Those leg pains got even worse: Paracetamol wouldn't touch them. Five nights it lasted, from the Sunday after my chemo until the next Thursday: five nights of pain, little sleep and feeling sorry for myself. There is *no* way I am going to let that happen again! I tell the Oncologist and she tells me that she will extend my steroids and get me a few nights' sleeping pills – at least she listened. She also offered to drop the dose of chemo for me, but I thought at this late stage that I should keep going with it. Chemo went well as usual, no major issues to report.

I admit I am a little scared of getting those pains again, but am trying not to think about it too much.

Final Chemo!!

Tuesday, 12 October 2009

I *so* can't believe today was my last chemo! It's a bit freaky, where have the last six months gone? Oh – the leg pains . . . Sleeping pills didn't work, and I had another five nights of sleeplessness, pain and crying. In the middle of it, I just kept telling myself that there was only one more chemo to go and then I was off to Spain!

Final chemo over, and I was quite emotional walking out of the day ward, all a bit strange. A nurse disconnected me from the drip, and I got up and walked out. That was that. I don't know how I feel, really – obviously glad it's all over, that I got through it, but also a bit of, 'Ok, what now?' kind of went through my mind. Anyway, I'm off to Spain in two days. *So* can't wait!

Saturday, November 1 2009

Well, Spain was just fantastic! Adam and Ann spoilt me rotten and they were very relieved to see me look so well, despite everything. It was the first time I had felt so well looked after throughout everything. I got breakfast in bed, dinner made for me and drinks brought to me – bliss! J I wore my wig when we went somewhere in the car, but apart from that I was boldly going bald . . . and didn't care who else in the street saw me, etc. Again, that felt good!

I was scared about being there and being in a lot of pain at night – however, this didn't happen. I had a few niggles, but nothing like I had experienced during chemo sessions four and five. I relaxed and dozed a lot and just took everything really slow. We even managed a day at the beach. Ok, it wasn't exactly hot, but I got there!

Spain was *the* best thing I could have done, for *me*!

I'm Glad that Chapter is Over!
Sunday, 29 November 2009

Well, chemo all over and done with. I haven't journalled here in ages, needed a break, ya know?

It's only check-ups now. God, do I feel vulnerable! No more bloods, no more tests, no more doctors – it's a bit scary, actually. First check-up will be in January sometime, I think.

It's weird, I know that my scan was clear, I know I have had my treatment, I know I have an 80 per cent chance of cure (a 20 per cent chance of antihistamines *non*-cure!!) . . . But every single ache or pain I get, the first thing I think is, 'Oh God, the cancer is back!' I have never been a hypochondriac – am I becoming one now? I ask my Macmillan counsellor that one, and she tells me it's a perfectly natural thought after my diagnosis, that most people with the same diagnosis think that too! Relief!

Officially in Remission
Wednesday, 20 January 2010

First Oncology check-up over and done with yesterday – thank God! All clear and looking good. It looks like I am a cancer survivor!! Next check-up in four months . . .

Why?
Tuesday, 21 June 2010

Today I had another huge shock. I had a private CT scan as a precaution (the NHS didn't feel I needed one), and today I was told I had a 5 cm secondary tumour on my liver. I couldn't speak, I just screamed –

this wasn't supposed to happen! I was *so* confident that I had beaten this disease, this horrible, cruel disease. My consultant was very shocked at this development, and also at my reaction it seems, as she wasn't able to answer the many questions I quick-fired at her . . . Am I now terminal? How long do I have – six months, a year? Is an operation possible? Why did this happen?

I left her office 20 minutes later in tears, unable to understand anything any more.

I was however told that an operation might be possible, and I am going to see a liver specialist next month. I don't feel able to be optimistic right now, though. I have a holiday to my friends in Spain already booked in July: should I go or not. . ?

Oops!
Thursday, 12 August 2010

I did go on holiday, after discussing it with the doctors concerned: they all agreed I should go, so I did. It was nice to get away: I was well looked after, but didn't have much energy.

And now, I'm in hospital. My bloods are very low and I need a blood transfusion – this is a new symptom! Since I've been in hospital, I've been getting very high temperatures (up to 41 °C), which are causing me some problems – mainly a symptom called 'rigors', which makes me shiver and feel unwell.

I ended up spending four weeks in hospital, while the medics conducted numerous tests, but were unable to find anything that could be causing the temperatures. This meant that I was not able to have the liver operation, and in fact the doctors were shocked at how much my tumour had grown by then . . . It was now too large for surgery to be an option any longer. I was gutted, as I knew surgery was my best chance.

Why is everything going wrong at the moment?

Even *More* Oops!!
Saturday, 25 September 2010

Today I felt a bit unwell and I vomited blood. I tried to stay calm though, and even had a snooze, thinking it was a one-off. But it wasn't: I ended up in hospital by 8.00 p.m., and was quite hysterical – not about vomiting blood, but about what was happening to me, to my body. I just kept on asking the doctors to knock me out, so that I would be unaware of what was going on. They obviously didn't do this, but they gave me blood, did some blood tests and moved me to the Cancer unit while they waited for the results. I was told I would have to have an endoscopy. Again, I screamed that I wanted to be knocked out for that!

Early the next morning, I was brought down to have the procedure. I was still screaming to be knocked out, and this time, I was . . .

I woke up two days later in Intensive Care. Apparently I had had anaphylactic shock after the procedure and I was very unwell. In a way I was lucky, as I didn't know anything about any of it. My poor brother saw it all, though. I was then transferred to the High Dependency Unit for a further three days and then back onto the Cancer Ward. They have no idea why I developed the anaphylactic shock: it could have been the blood I was given, or the anaesthetic, but they couldn't be sure. Do they know *anything*??

I spent another four weeks in hospital after that, getting weaker by the day. My appetite disappeared and even the *smell* of hospital food made me sick. After two weeks, I was begging to get home but they just kept telling me I wasn't well enough.

Hoorah!
Thursday, 9 December 2010

Today, I was allowed home – I am still very weak, but very determined. My next chemotherapy treatment is due to commence on 20 December, whoopee do! I have been prescribed Paclitaxel on a weekly basis for 18 weeks, this time at a reduced dose. This means saying goodbye to my hair again . . . great!

I was able to get a 'home from hospital' service via the Hospital social worker, and someone came to see me daily to make sure I ate something and that I was ok. I also had community nurses coming in every night, to make sure I could get to bed (if I had been out of it at all, that is!).

It really did hit me how difficult it is, living on your own when you are very ill. It was actually frightening sometimes. What if I fell? What if I couldn't get to the loo? These were very real fears, but the care I received really helped and made me feel more secure and confident as each week went by.

Hoorah Again!
Monday, 31 January 2011

Today I had treatment Number Seven, and also got the results of my CT Scan following treatment Number Six. My tumour has got a bit smaller, and the *best* news is that my blood tumour marker (CA125), which was 500 back in June 2009 when I was first diagnosed, and had risen to over 3000 while I was in hospital, has now dropped down to just 147!! This can only be good!

Back to Work
Tuesday, 1 February 2011

Who would have believed this: I am back at work today! My last day at work before this was 13 August last year, and now here I am – back again at last. It was *so* good to be able to be work – only 2 days this week, but I will increase this as time and my treatment progresses, so long as I can cope with it.

I finally feel as if I can now have some normality to my life again. I am feeling stronger every week, and the doctors and nurses keep telling me I am looking fabulous. Sure, I knew that already!

I Feel Great!!
Monday, 21 February 2011

As I have been improving every week and the treatment is going so well, I asked a *big* question today at treatment. I was a bit scared of the answer, but felt I needed to ask it anyway. The question was: will it be possible for liver surgery to be considered again, given that my treatment is working?

I was told that my medical notes would have to be looked at again in depth, that a scan would have to be carried out at the end of treatment (in six weeks' time) and then a medical team meeting would have to be held. However, I was told, a full discussion would indeed be possible and, as long as we could convince a surgeon that such a measure was worthwhile, all should be fine!

I liked that answer. At least it wasn't an immediate 'no'.

Today, I feel good. I'm now doing three days a week at work, and I hope to increase that to four days in another fortnight or so.

I had such a very rough time last summer, but I have come through it, like the fighter I am. I am *still* a cancer survivor!

Pauline Hamilton
Ovarian Cancer, 2009

A Second Chance at Life

Ryan Hubbard
Testicular Cancer, 2007

1. Diagnosis

What goes through someone's mind when they hear the word 'cancer'? Well, it probably differs for everyone, depending on whether you have it yourself, know someone who has or it is something which has never affected you personally or anyone close to you.

The word 'cancer' invokes fear in most people. To be fair, most people don't understand it. Why would they? There are so many different types of cancer that it must only be confusing to anyone outside of the loop. Anyone who hasn't seen it affect someone they know doesn't want to know what it's about! And I don't blame them either. One thing I think everyone would agree on is that the word 'cancer' is more or less synonymous with death! I've seen the destruction the illness can cause in front of my own eyes – you also see it in the media, with celebrities contracting the disease and paying the consequences. Add to that the internet and even word of mouth, and death and destruction is nearly all you can associate with the word.

Whenever the day came when I was diagnosed myself, I don't think I felt anything or thought anything. It was as if I was numb to the core, and for a brief time, my mind tried to block the word out and ignore it. The day I found out I had testicular cancer was 14 August 2007, exactly a month before my 21st birthday!

I had been sitting in a busy hospital waiting room, itching to be seen. Now, I'm never usually like this, because I've been to my fair share of hospitals over the years, but this day was different. As soon as I stepped through the front door of the hospital, I tried to remain calm, but the butterflies in my stomach were in overdrive and the palms of my hands were sweaty. Deep down, I believed everything was going to be ok, but as on any occasion when visiting a hospital, there is always that niggling doubt.

Either way, I was there to get a diagnosis, which was good, as it had been all I had been thinking about for weeks and it was really starting to get to me! I was finally going to get an answer.

It was one month before this day that I had gone to the GP about a lump I had found – this was to lead to one of the most eventful days of my life, but for all the wrong reasons! When my GP told me he was referring me to the hospital, I knew then that there was a chance of bad news. I just hoped that wouldn't be the case, though.

I never told anyone about the appointment. Why put all that worry on family and friends, when there might not be anything to worry about? Looking back on it, I wish I had told someone – anyone, in fact. It would have taken a lot of that pressure off my shoulders, let me tell you. My name was finally called and I was up like a shot, eager to get in there and be told all was fine. How wrong I was! Within seconds of the doctor examining me, he called in the consultant and he didn't waste any time in telling me that I had testicular cancer.

Nothing could have prepared me for that moment – nothing! I immediately burst into tears. I didn't know what to do. To tell the truth, it felt as though it was a dream and I was the only one in that room. Nothing they said after that first moment would register in my brain. In one ear and out of the other, as they say. I'd never been in this kind of situation before, so understandably I couldn't work out how I was going to get through this. Here I was in a hospital room, trying to get my head around what I'd just been told, and all the while life was still going on around me. Everyone was trying to prepare me for the next part of the process, and yet, I was oblivious.

Once the outburst of tears had ceased, everything started to become clearer for me. Even though I was still scared and confused, I felt as though I had come out of my dream again, and I was ready to face the next step. Doctors were coming in and out, as were the nurses who, at the same time, were talking to me, trying to find the words to say that I was going to be alright. I didn't want to hear it. I was still trying to block out the truth: it was like I was a child, wanting to put my hands over my ears and hoping it would go away! But this was really happening, and I was going to have to try and deal with it. Things went very quick from then on in, that day. An ultrasound was done, as well as blood tests, to start to piece together just how bad the cancer might be.

Once I got through all that, I was pretty much free to go. Only one thing was stopping me, and that was my state of mind: I had been put through a lot in a very short space of time. That kind of shock to the system would affect anyone, so much so that the staff were worried that driving home might not be such a good idea for me.

Because my parents were away on vacation, I rang my boss to ask him to pick me up. Obviously I had to tell him what had just happened, which wasn't easy. He left work immediately and came to the hospital. By the time he arrived, I had settled down quite a bit. He didn't know what to say, which wasn't surprising. On a normal day I would find it hard to talk about personal health issues myself, so for him, trying to bring the topic up and remain positive at the same time must have been a nightmare. If I had been in my boss's shoes, I don't know how I would have reacted. I suppose no one knows until the situation arises.

I got home, feeling surprisingly good. I wanted to be alone to collect my thoughts. As for my mother and father, it didn't seem right to tell them the news over the phone, and they were due home that night anyway, so I decided to wait. It sounds stupid, but I dreaded the thought of telling them. I knew they would support me all the way, but part of me couldn't stand the thought them knowing. I felt as though it would ruin their holiday.

My parents arrived home around midnight, and they knew something was wrong straight away. There was no way of getting around it: they had to know. I had lied to them about the appointment – well I never told them about it – but I couldn't do the same about this. I couldn't keep what I knew now to myself. If it was going to be a tough few months, I was going to need all the help and support I could get! When I did tell them, of course they were in shock, but once again, I felt as though I was in a trance and everyone else faded out again, so their emotions weren't as clear to me as they should have been.

The following day I felt surprisingly good. I had slept very well and during the morning, I managed to convince myself that cancer would be no worse than any other challenge I've faced in my lifetime. You may think 'challenge' is an interesting word to use, but the way I see it, if I can go up against the cancer head-to-head, it will be a way for me to fight it. If I pretend it's a competition, whereby I have to beat the cancer, I will.

Taking this idea further, it's my own personal war: my body and my mind fighting against the cancer, for the good of my health.

Although I hadn't been through any other kind of procedure or treatment before I was diagnosed, I believe there can be nothing harder than beating cancer. Now that I knew that in my own mind, it would allow me to prepare for what would be the hardest few months of my life. I also believed that if I prepared for the worse possible scenario, I would be a stronger person at the end of the ordeal. This was my way of dealing with it. I also tried to gather as much information as possible, to try and understand what I was in for. I realise that some people wouldn't want to know and that my way isn't the only way of dealing with it. Everyone has their own approach, but there are some things that you should definitely do to try and make life easier for yourself.

Firstly, keep the lines of communication open. Make sure you maintain open, two-way communication with loved ones, doctors, and so on after your diagnosis. If you don't, you may feel isolated. The more you know and the more honest you are about your own emotions, the better you will feel.

Anticipate possible physical changes. After your diagnosis and before you begin treatment is the best time to plan for changes, in my experience. If you are prepared in this way, you will cope better if and when anything actually happens. For example, hair loss is fairly common and this could be something that worries you, so act now before it becomes yet another shock to deal with!

As well as maintaining a healthy lifestyle, try and keep your everyday life as normal as possible. It might sound hard and believe me, it is, but if you can keep to a normal routine, it will help you feel like everything is as it was before the diagnosis. Although some days this might not be possible – and that's ok too. Take one day at a time. It's easy to overlook this simple strategy during such a stressful time.

Finally, review your goals and priorities. This is a time when you realise what's really important in your life. Find time for the activities that are most important to you and give you the most sense of meaning.

Other things may come to mind but what I've said here may get you started through the tough and stressful time that is a cancer diagnosis.

2. Fear

Cancer can throw up a wave of emotions, but usually the first thing that strikes is fear. I don't know whether it is the thought that you might have a shortened life span, or the idea of the pain and suffering you may have to endure if chemotherapy or radiotherapy is on the cards. It's hard to pinpoint. In modern times, cancer has become more common (more so than many of us would like) and so the fear of it has lessened to some extent – but not so many years ago, the fear of cancer was very widespread, since death was more common then and it was known to be a terrible disease which was very difficult to overcome. At least now, cancer is treatable in most cases, and many patients are being given a second chance at life.

Knowing all of this doesn't really help though with the fear that runs wild in our dreams when we are trying to understand what is happening to us! With so much to worry about, it's important to try and get your head around the cancer as soon as possible. It would be very easy to lose control of your fear altogether, and just feel like your world is over and there is nothing left to live for. If this happens, you need to be strong and snap out of it. Easier said than done, but it is vital!

When I was told I had cancer, my emotions were so topsy-turvy to begin with that I didn't know where I stood. Once things began to sink in though, I was scared stiff – anyone would be. All I could think of was whether or not I would die! This was impossible to predict in my case, as not even the doctors knew the true extent of the cancer. Once I had been briefed by the doctors and told all about the cancer I had and what I was to expect, I realised that I had to let go of my fear before it ate me from the inside out. I knew I needed all my strength to get through this, and being scared was only going to make matters worse. I managed to keep this up for the couple of weeks I had to wait for my biopsy results. Luckily for me, my results were fairly good. I had a good chance of making a full recovery, although I was going to need chemo. If things had been different – as in, the results had been much worse, the fear that was so strong within me might have bubbled to the surface again!

Even through my chemotherapy, I had moments where I feared for my life, times when I really didn't believe I was going to survive. One occasion was when my white blood count was very low – which was to be expected. However, to make sure it didn't get to levels where it would be dangerous, I had to have an injection which was supposed to boost my white blood count. Unluckily for me, I took a severe reaction to it during the night and felt as though my back was going to explode! I was screaming the house down, the pain was unbearable and the fear I felt during that episode was as bad as it has ever been. No matter how strong I had been up to that point, I couldn't control myself any more: I was terrified! Luckily the doctor on duty managed to deal with the situation and I was given other medication to do the same job but without side effects. It was rare to react in the way I had, but not impossible, and I just happened to be one of the people that did.

It is impossible to be positive all the time: there are always going to be moments when you just can't help but feel afraid, or even terrified. I thought I knew what fear was, until I heard the words 'You have cancer'. Real fear came with an unmistakeable sensation which made my previous fears seem very minor in comparison. It's ok to feel this way, and you will know yourself when the fear is controllable and when it isn't.

There will be days when you feel great and are able to forget everything that is going on – but there will be times too when you can think of nothing but what is happening to you. If you can have more good days than bad, fear will slowly dwindle and before you know it, there will be light at the end of the tunnel. Things will get back to normal and all being well, you will go on to live the rest of your life. You will become a stronger person by having to live with the fear you have encountered through cancer. No matter what life throws at you in the future, you will not have the same level of fear again. Use this to your advantage while you can.

3. Family and Friends

We all need friends and family, but never more so than during the experience of cancer. Having close and supportive relationships helps us navigate the rough waters of diagnosis, treatment and recovery. During the struggle with cancer, our need for friendship and family support intensifies.

Although friends and family are there for you during the experience, it might not necessarily feel like that to begin with. The fact is that many people, including our friends and family, don't understand cancer or know how to deal with it. You may think they have withdrawn from you, or they may not speak to you as much, but this isn't because they don't care – it's because they may feel helpless, and they are probably afraid of saying or doing the wrong things. Therefore they won't say anything. Once they begin to understand more, they will most likely come round, and not only will they confront their own fears about cancer, but they will be more supportive too.

During my ordeal, I have to confess that I didn't really notice what my family were doing for me to begin with. I think I needed to understand for myself what was going on first and prepare myself for the months ahead before I could accept the help of my family. After that initial few days, I did come round and really started to notice how my family were trying to help me. Of course my mum and dad were at the front line, there for me every step of the way. I had to make sure they knew exactly what was happening. It was hard enough for me, not knowing what I was to face; I could hardly imagine what they were going through. If I knew, they knew, and this it helped a lot.

For example, when I was told that I could lose my hair, the doctors mentioned that this might start happening about three weeks after my first round of chemo. I was apprehensive and not sure what to expect, but when it happened bang on schedule, at least I wasn't as surprised by it – nor were my parents. They took it in their stride, which made me feel much better about it all. Of course, at first I didn't like what had happened, but with their support I got used to it, and in the end I wasn't afraid to show the world.

If I hadn't informed my parents of this possibility in advance, they might have reacted differently. As mums do, mine fussed over me from the start. For example, when I returned home after the first cycle of chemo, my mum had disinfected the whole house! Both of my parents visited at least once a day during my stays in hospital, and when I was really poorly, they did everything they could to make me feel as comfortable and as human as possible through a very tough time!

You may be saying to yourself that this is what you would expect from immediate family. Perhaps that is so, but you only realise just how important this type of input is when you go through something like cancer. As for the rest of my family, what can I say? They were brilliant. They didn't smother me nor did they pretend nothing had happened. What they did do during the times I spent with them was to try to make me forget all that was happening. They would talk about anything and everything, and try to distract me from the pain and suffering I was dealing with. Some I saw more than others, but with my immune system becoming weaker and weaker as time went on, it became harder to have visitors, in case they had a cough or cold and so on. Anyway, they made life much easier for me and, without that family support, it wouldn't be worth thinking about just how hard the whole ordeal would have been!

Trying to tell my friends was a whole different kettle of fish, though. Those closest to me had to be told, but somehow I didn't know how to go about it. The first few days after the diagnosis, I kept to myself. I had so much to try and get my head around that I couldn't find the time to tell them. But it had to be done. I had ignored calls and texts and it was only a matter of time before they would start to ask questions. But the dilemma I had was, how do I go about it? It isn't something that you just bring up in normal conversation! At that particular time, I wasn't good emotionally, as you might expect. I was pretty sure that if I met any of my friends face-to-face, I was bound to break down and I didn't want that. It wasn't as if I was trying to be the hard man and not show my emotions – I didn't really care about that. I had worse things to worry about! I think I felt that if it was to happen (me breaking down, that is), it might make the whole situation harder. What I mean by that is, my friends might get very uncomfortable with what they had just learned and not know what to do and, through no fault of their own, distance themselves from me when I needed them most!

At the end of the day however, they were my friends and I needed their support. I thought that if I could show that I was strong and ready for the battle ahead of me, it might make it easier for them to accept. Of course, it's never as easy as that. Everybody who has to hear news like that will react differently. I just hoped that they would all take it well. I knew that when I told each of them, I would soon find out just who my friends were!

Everybody who goes through cancer will probably experience this. It's hard to accept when some friends seem to disappear during your time with cancer, but what can you do? You just have to make sure you get yourself better and make the most of the friends you still have. I was lucky that all of my closest friends stood by me, through thick and thin. Instead of meeting with them and telling them the news, I rang each of them. Some people might think that is the wrong way to go about it, but it felt comfortable for me. Each of these friends took it differently, but they were there for me and would do anything I needed. Some visited me in hospital, some came to the house when I was in no fit state to leave. Others picked me up and brought me out. It was the simple things they did that really helped. The regular phone calls or the words of encouragement always worked!

When I was in hospital for my operation, my friend's dad, who is a minister, came to visit me. I'm not religious in any way, but he asked if he could say a prayer. I had no problem with that – in fact, it helped a great deal. The fact he had such faith and thought it would do good was enough to raise my spirits. Moments like that made the journey a little easier. Without my friends, it would have been an incredibly tough time. Your family is always there but your friends make life more like normal. Even if they make one minute of your day easier, it makes all the difference. They know who they are and I'm very grateful to every one of them. I will never forget what they did. Hopefully I can repay the favour at some point.

4. Treatment

With any cancer, some sort of treatment is usually needed to destroy whatever mutant cells are roaming about the body! Both radiotherapy and chemotherapy are common treatments used. Both also bring their fair share of controversy for being incredibly damaging to the body. I've heard the phrase 'slash and burn' being used to describe chemotherapy! Although both do damage in the short term, they will usually save your life in the long term.

Once my particular type of cancer was identified, the doctors decided that I needed chemotherapy. I had heard all the stories beforehand, but didn't want to take note. I knew it was going to be tough – but only time would tell just how bad it would be!

I was to have 'BEP chemotherapy', which is named after the chemo drugs used. These are: **Bleomycin**, **Etoposide** and **Cisplatin**. I was to have three cycles, each lasting three weeks. When I was starting the first cycle, my body was still recovering from surgery and I had lost a lot of weight, so I wasn't sure just how I would cope.

The treatment didn't start the way I had expected. I arrived early Sunday morning, was settled onto the ward and bloods were taken. Before anything else could be done, I had to wait for the blood results. I was free to leave and come back later. This is one of the most frustrating things about chemo – the waiting! Time went slowly enough, and waiting around only made matters worse. I came back later to be put onto a drip. I had to have a drip for 24 hours to flush out my kidneys in preparation for the first dose of chemo. You would think lying about, watching TV, reading a book and playing computer games would be a nice break from the daily grind but after a couple of hours, it drives you mad. I had another couple of days of this ahead of me. I can moan about it now, as I'm fit and healthy and can't sit still, and can choose when I want to relax, but when you're in hospital with cancer, you have no choice in the matter, especially when the chemo kicks in and you're tired and weak. Chemotherapy makes you appreciate your freedom, as it takes it all away at times.

My chemo started the following day, with Etoposide and Cisplatin. The next day, all three drugs were given and on the third day, Etoposide on its own. This dose of drugs began to take its toll. It was probably the worst during my three spells in hospital (three days at the start of each cycle and a short stay for a quick dose of chemo drugs on each of the second weeks). At the end of the day, these drugs are poison and it wouldn't matter what chemotherapy drugs they were. They're so poisonous that the nurses administering the drugs have to wear arm-length gloves, aprons and goggles to protect themselves! When I saw this, that's when it sunk in for me just how dangerous this stuff was. If any of these drugs were to get on your skin, it would burn: so God knows what they were going to do on the inside!

This was a worry, but on the upside this treatment was going to save my life! That's the most important thing to remember if you have to go through chemotherapy. No matter how much you suffer and just wish it would end, you will have your life back afterwards and will be able to go back to living again. You will be so grateful when you are back to full health that it will have seemed worth it. It's hard to believe at the start, but if you keep these positive thoughts in your mind, all will become clear.

As for the remainder of each cycle, I would rest at home after the hospital stay. The start of the following week, I would return for one day and then I would rest for the remaining days of the week, with no chemo during the third week, so that my body could try and rebuild my immune system before the attack of the next cycle. As far as I know, all cancer treatments come with the risk of some type of side effects. That doesn't mean you will always suffer from them. Some people get through their treatment with little or no side effects, while at the other end of the scale, other people suffer with lots of side effects. Everyone is different, so don't assume you're always going to be as sick as a parrot and bedridden. It might not happen at all – and if it doesn't, I'm so pleased for you. I only wish I had been that lucky.

My time with chemo was full of its fair share of ups and downs. I had a long list of side effects myself, including the usual suspects: hair loss, sickness and nausea. They were terrible. I got used to the hair loss pretty quickly. The initial stages were tough, but once I got used to the idea, I carried on as if it hadn't happened. Easier said than done, I know, but if you try and make it look as though it doesn't bother you, other people around you won't carry on as if it's a big deal either. It worked for me anyway. Sickness and nausea – what can I say? They speak for themselves. It's horrible and has left me terrified to this day of ever being sick again!

Other side effects which hit me hard were loss of taste, pins and needles, back pain and fatigue. I've always enjoyed my food, so to lose my sense of taste was a nightmare. Everything I had enjoyed before tasted of metal. Meat, chocolate, fruit and veg – it all tasted the same. The only time I got any enjoyment from food was when it was really hot! Chilli made my time through chemo slightly easier. I needed to keep my weight up, which was hard when food was tasteless, but chilli or curry and so on gave me something to taste.

Pins and needles were one of the very first side effects I had, which was quite scary. About an hour after starting chemo, my body started to go all tingly. I didn't know what to think at first, but the doctors told me it was ok. It felt like it was the chemo pumping through my veins: odd and probably not the case, but this was the only thing I could think of that might be causing the problem. The back pain I suffered was brought on from the fact that my white blood count was low. I was given a booster injection that I overreacted to, which is quite rare, I was told. My back felt as though it was going to break in two, due to the bone marrow being in overdrive. This whole episode was one of the most painful experiences of my life.

The last and the most difficult side effect which I had to deal with was fatigue! Most people report this as one of the worst side effects for them. The only way to get around it is plenty of rest. Your body basically shuts down and even if you want to do something, you just can't. You might sleep 15 hours a day and still feel tired. The chemo works its way through the body and sleeping gives your body a chance to try and recuperate and mend itself. Even on days when I thought I felt strong enough to go outside, I would just manage a short walk and then I would need to go straight to bed. I was shattered all the time and even after treatment, it took me six months to fully recover and feel myself again.

Until you actually experience this, you won't be able to understand what I mean. All I can say is that if you're about to go through chemotherapy, get yourself prepared for the possible side effects that might be common with your particular cancer. Don't be naïve in thinking you won't experience any, as it will only be a shock if you do – which is exactly what you don't want during this critical stage.

You are only prescribed chemotherapy when it gives you a considerably better chance of survival. Because it's so toxic, it's not just given to everybody. If you are told that chemo is the right treatment for you, just think of how much of a better chance of survival you have.

What most people don't realise either is that undergoing surgery will increase your chances of a full recovery even more than just chemo or radiotherapy. I found that quite hard to believe at first, but apparently it's true. Surgery itself – any kind of surgery – is tough. When your life hangs in the balance and you are about to go under the knife, you can't help thinking, 'Will I open my eyes again?' Your emotions are in overdrive, of course.

For me, surgery was the first major step in the treatment process (although this is not necessarily the case for everyone). I can't say enough about my surgeon – he really helped me on the way to recovery. The relief I felt to wake up after the operation and realise that most of the cancer had been removed was unbelievable! I felt like I was breaking down the cancer's defences and needed just one more push for victory! The pain that I had immediately after my surgery wasn't so pleasant, but in some ways, even going through this was a comfort, as I knew that the battle I had set myself up for had finally begun, and I could now start to prepare in many other ways for what was yet to come.

Don't be afraid of pain: it's the body's natural reaction which lets you know something is wrong and needs attention. Some people try to ignore it, brush it under the table and hope it goes away. It's always a sign that something is up. Going through the pain of cancer opens your eyes, and any time you feel pain after such a journey, you automatically want to know what the problem is, and if it is serious. You should know your own body and if something doesn't feel right, you're better being safe than sorry. So pain can sometimes help. It did for me, as I might never have gone to the doctor in the first place otherwise!

5. Support

I've already mentioned friends and family as a means of support during cancer, but support can come from many other sources and it must be taken when it is offered, as every little helps during this hard time. During my time in hospital, I received great support from the doctors and nurses who looked after me. You would assume that this would happen anyway – yes, but it all depends on the individual patient too, and how much help they are willing to receive. The nurses who cared for me couldn't have done a better job. It was the little things they did that really helped me through. They were able to work me out fairly quickly and they would somehow know if I was feeling down. I was in a bit of a hole quite a few times during my stays in the cancer centre. When my friends and family weren't there, the nurses would step in and try and cheer me up and somehow make life easier. They could see what cancer does to people on a daily basis, so they knew the importance of supporting their patients.

I would have the nurses running about for me – not, I should add, because I felt like it, but due to the fact I wasn't fit enough to do much for myself – I relied on them to help me. They did so without a thought and I'm very grateful for that. It may be their job, but to do such a job takes a very special individual. It is in their nature to help you and when they do, it really makes a difference. I found the nurses' support usually came at a time when I needed it most. I was pretty ill during my stays in hospital, so I needed help to keep me going. There would have been days when I was depressed to the max, and then laughing my head off, all because a nurse was there and trying to cheer me up. Don't be afraid to make use of that support: they will (do their best to) help you!

Doctors were always very good to me, too. They knew exactly what to say, told me everything that was going to happen. They were aware that it was going to be a hard road ahead for me, and they offered their advice as to how to cope. I understand that not everyone gets this kind of treatment from their doctors. From speaking to other cancer patients, I've heard some pretty shocking stories – about how their consultants didn't seem to care, how they saw them as just another number! This isn't always the case, however. Doctors are busy people and even if they can't always be there when you need them, someone else will be –whether it's a member of their team, or a nurse, and so on. Their main priority is to save your life and if they can do that, that's a good start. They will offer you support, and even in small doses this can go a long way. If they tell you that you're looking much better, that your results are all clear, that you're on your way to a full recovery, and they congratulate you, and so on – it's all still support and without it, none of us would get very far!

One thing I found hard to deal with was my financial situation – how I was going to pay the bills, etc., while I was off work. Financial support is essential too of course, but at the time I was more worried about my health and didn't really have the time or strength to think about it.

I was asked whether I wanted a social worker, and I agreed to this. I don't know if everyone receives this kind of care, but I was under the impression that this was standard practice. A social worker does many things for you and it is only when you're stuck in hospital that you realise how much you have on your plate. I don't know whether the hospital staff knew I felt like this and so offered to put the social worker on to me, but obviously everyone copes differently and perhaps I was showing the strain. Whatever happened, I was glad to get a social worker. I think that, because I didn't know this person, I somehow found it much easier to talk to them about stuff. When trying to talk about things to friends and family, sometimes things get awkward. When speaking to a professional who has heard it all before, you know you'll be listened to and have none of the 'baggage' to deal with afterwards!

The social worker was the one who initially steered the conversation towards finances. I knew that money was going to be tight – my sick pay was horrendous and my income had dried up completely, due to being unfit to work – so I was in desperate need of help. The social worker knew how to progress my case and very quickly got it sorted. Before I knew it, I was getting grants from charities of various kinds. All this automatically eased the worries I had about such things. The road ahead was tough enough, but the financial strain could have really crippled me. Now I was free to concentrate what strength I had on fighting this terrible illness.

I was lucky I didn't own a house, have kids or have my own business. If you do and you also have cancer, ask for a social worker, as they do wonders. The way I saw it, it wasn't my fault that I got cancer. I still wanted to work but couldn't, so why should I have had to suffer any more than I was already? Well, you shouldn't have to either. All the more reason to take whatever help is available. Sometimes it's hard to do so, but you've got to remember the situation you are in: can you afford not to accept the support?

It's amazing when I think about it now, but I used to always take charities for granted. After cancer, I wanted to do my bit for them, as I felt it was the right thing to do. They offered me brilliant support and without them, things could have been a lot harder. When I started to get involved with the Friends of the Cancer Centre, I soon started to see the great work they do. Many cancer patients relied on their help within the cancer centre. Without their fundraising work, the standard of care would have fallen, and that would have affected the patients. The support I received made me want to give back in some way, and I did so through fundraising of my own.

Support comes from many different sources, but every single one of these is as important as the others. Your journey through cancer would be incredibly hard all on your own. Support takes the pressure off you and your job of fighting the illness becomes much easier. I truly believe that without the support I was given, I mightn't be in the situation I'm in now! I was lucky that my prognosis was very good, but if it hadn't have been and I hadn't had any support from others, I don't think I would have had the will to keep going. Support pushes you on and makes you believe in yourself. If that isn't a good enough reason to make the most of it, I don't know what is!

6. Thoughts and Feelings

As during any critical stage in your life, your thoughts and feelings will be in overdrive during your time with cancer. You will experience emotions you never thought you could feel; you will think and feel differently than you would have before.

I think it's fair to say that feeling anxious at any time during this whole experience is very common. You are constantly worrying about test results, treatment or even about when your next dose of painkillers is coming! This is all fine. After your cancer journey, you will probably find you never feel anxious again – or at least not to the same extent: nothing else will come close. So, don't feel like the world will come crashing down on you if you are anxious. Things will get better! On my journey, I got very depressed at times. Well, I say depressed – I was never diagnosed with depression, but it sure felt like depression to me. I became very negative at times, and I would think everyone was against me. I would sink deeper into a low mood and would sometimes find it very difficult to get out of. Let's just say cancer does that, whether you like it or not – it can't be helped. I've found that even after your treatment is over, and even a year or two down the line, feeling depressed is still a part of life. The thought of cancer will never leave you. Whether it's through a scar or through memory, it's always there, so to get down in the dumps about it every now again isn't unknown. The more you come to terms with what has happened, the more your depressed state of mind will lift, and your topsy-turvy thoughts and feelings should hopefully get back to a more manageable state!

Low self-esteem and feeling self-conscious is, I think, all part of anyone's experience of cancer. If you need treatment through surgery, chemo or radiotherapy, these feelings are especially true. When you're left with scars, bleached skin or other blemishes due to cancer, you can't help but feel self-conscious and that can lead to you feeling bad about yourself. I'm only starting to get my confidence back and that's nearly three years of being cancer-free. I hated myself and my body for a long time, but eventually I got to the stage where I thought to myself that if people can't accept me for who I now am, they aren't worth it. It's terrible to feel like that, these are possibly the worst feelings to have, as they trigger so many others. Cancer is a nasty illness, but if you get a second chance at life, no matter how you now look or think you look, you are still alive, and that should be enough to convince you, at the end of the day, that thinking like that isn't worth it any more. If cancer teaches you one thing, that is to live life like every day is your last. All those worries will slowly dwindle away. It's hard and takes time, but that's all part of the recovery, so don't try and rush things. Everything will work out in the end and when it does, you will feel so happy!

Emotions are something I've talked about a lot here but they are something you shouldn't be afraid of showing. I was never all that emotional before this. I had a tendency to bottle things up, but cancer makes you get all those worries out. It can't be helped: you have so much on your mind! I cried a hell of a lot, as I felt I just couldn't cope at times. I would always feel so much better for it afterwards. I found it easier to talk about my problems then, which made me feel like a huge weight had been lifted off my shoulders. I bet that most of you who have read this and have had cancer will have been like this too at times. Crying is a natural way to release emotions that you shouldn't hold back on. No one will think differently of you. I wouldn't cry very often now, but if something really upsets me, I don't fight it – and neither should you. You feel bad enough as it is when cancer strikes, but to feel the weight of the world again when there is no need – why let it happen? Let it all out and feel happy again. You owe it to yourself to feel happy, especially after the miserable time you may have had, or are still having.

7. Life after Cancer

Everybody talks about how tough cancer is. Whether it is the diagnosis, the treatment or just the pure fear it brings, all the components that make up the experience of cancer are tough. But nobody really talks about what can be the toughest component of all in some ways – and that is life after cancer! The more people I talk to who have had cancer, the more they all keep saying the same thing, and that is that in many senses, they probably struggled more once they tried to get their lives back on track than they did during the experience of cancer itself.

For someone who hasn't had to go through the hell of cancer, the concept of finding life hard after cancer can seem almost impossible to understand. This is why I find it a very important point to bring up. For anyone unfortunate enough to be going through cancer, the reality of this can be quite daunting, but I personally feel that if you are made aware of this beforehand, it can only better prepare you for it. If I had known how hard life after cancer would be before the event, it might have helped me to face my fears better than I was able to do!

When my chemotherapy finished at the end of November 2007, I went through a period of time when I felt left in the dark. The time when hospital visits never seemed to end finished all of a sudden, or so it felt. I felt vulnerable and afraid. I thought that the cancer might return at any minute. It was as if I had been forgotten about. And in some ways, you are. The medical staff have treated you and all seems to be ok, so while that's the case, they must concentrate their efforts on others that are in a much worse situation. In reality though, you aren't left behind – it only feels like it. But the lack of medical attention which comes after cancer – when before it was constant – is a bit of a shock to the system, and this is where the problems can start.

I was soon to realise the pressures I was now facing. During my treatment, I never really had much time to think what was happening to me! I was too busy concentrating on getting myself better. Once the treatment finished, it hit me very hard and I struggled to cope. It brought so many other pressures: to be honest, a long list that would take a long time to explain. I was very insecure and just felt rubbish, really. The thought of cancer and what it did to me took its toll very quickly and I began to hate myself. For a very long time, I was a wreck. I didn't know who to talk to. I hated myself for what I had become and I didn't know why. It was a constant struggle and although I was getting fitter and stronger day after day physically, I just couldn't get myself out of the hole I was in emotionally. The bad memories haunted me, the scars haunted me, seeing people die from cancer haunted me – and I couldn't get it out of my head. Not a day went by that I didn't think about it. It soon got to the stage where I realised I had to do something about it!

Getting back to work was a start. Having a routine again really helped keep my mind on what I had to do, rather than the doom and gloom I was feeling all the time. Even though to start with, I couldn't really do very much because I was so weak, the little I could do really boosted my spirits, and the more work I did, the happier I became. I was starting to feel normal again. Mentally I was still suffering though, and I needed to find other ways to help. Speaking to other cancer survivors really did the trick, I found. Trying to talk to anybody doesn't quite do the job sometimes, as you feel that unless they've been through what you have, they won't understand – so a fellow survivor can really get you out of the rut.

One way in which I decided to try and help me get back to normal and feel better about myself was to take part in a cancer fundraiser for a local charity. I decided to do a 24-hour mountain bike race in Scotland, along with two friends. I organised everything and along with all the training I had to do, my mind was starting to think of better things. I was getting better and I could see the benefits and that I was finally getting back to normal! We completed the race less than a year from my finishing treatment – ten months in fact – but it took all that time to recuperate and feel partially normal again. It's a long, drawn-out affair but once I got to the point where it wasn't dominating me anymore, I could slowly move on with my life. It's a lot like the way I described the whole situation in Section One here – I see it as a war.

My experience of cancer can only be described as a war between my mind and body. So much of my physical strength was taken away by my experience. I fought long and hard to get back to the way I was before the diagnosis. With every minute becoming harder and harder, in some ways I found myself thinking that cancer won the war, in the sense that I didn't feel anything like the person I once was. My mind couldn't take it all in and my body was getting weaker and weaker: I thought the cancer was winning. Now I'm out on the other side and fighting fit and healthy, I still feel like a different person but I can accept that, as I think cancer has made me stronger mentally. Although my experience was one I never hope to have to go through again, in a way I'm glad I've been through it. Not because of the pain and suffering involved, but because of how I've battled through it in a way I never thought I could. That inner strength and self-belief made me realise I can get through anything.

Three years on, and I still firmly believe that. My life is different. Whether it's for the better, I don't know, but I'm finally starting to feel happy again. It took a long time, but at least there was a light at the end of the tunnel. I look at my life differently now, thanks to cancer. I would say it's a gift – a lousy one, but one that really tests you to the limit and if you come out the other side, you will really understand what life is about. Most people don't have a chance to look at their life without all the blinkers on. You may still be left with the scars or the nightmares, but you still have your life and that's the most important thing. Look after it, it should mean so much more now, if it didn't before!

Ryan Hubbard
Testicular Cancer, 2007

Cancer Diagnosis

I froze time, everything seemed to stop at that moment.
I cried like I've never cried before.
I thought that the life I had lived to that point was never going to be
    the same,
I cried again.
I thought my head was going to explode
I heard many words and phrases, none of which I wanted to hear.
I felt like I woke up and had a dream
I cried once more when I realised this was *real*
I worried how this might affect those close to me
I cried again at that thought.
I decided to take a stand and beat this
I knew from that point I was going to win the war
I felt relieved, like a weight was lifted off my shoulders
I then took each day like it was my last and now I'm through to the
    other side!

Ryan Hubbard

The 'Big Guns'

Alex Lineham
Leiomyosarcoma, July 2008 & April 2009

Alex Lineham's battle with cancer ended in September 2010. She will always be remembered by all the members of the HOPE Cancer Support Group for the encouragement she so readily gave to each one of them, and for her determination to live life to the full, even in the face of great uncertainty.

Cancer was not really a word in my vocabulary prior to July 2008. Sure, I knew people who had had cancer – friends of my parents, people I hadn't seen in years – but no-one particularly close to me. So cancer had never really impacted my life in a significant way.

That all changed when, as a result of a routine operation, a pathologist made an 'incidental finding' of leiomyosarcoma. To this day, I count myself very lucky that I had that routine operation, because, although it changed my life forever and there was nothing routine about the outcome, having the operation meant that I had effectively bought myself a considerable amount of time.

I was living in New Zealand at the time. My husband and I had married less than a year earlier and had left the UK to set up home on the other side of the planet. A wise move, we thought: a lifestyle change. We got a lot more change than we bargained for when I took sick just months after our arrival in the 'the land of the long white cloud'.

The 'Kiwis' aren't pessimists – nor are they optimists. They just tend to tell it like it is, straight-down-the-middle. So when I got a call from a nurse in the Wellington hospital on a Friday afternoon, saying that they had 'forgotten' to tell me to come in for a two-week post-op check, I should have thought nothing of it. However, that little voice inside my head told me something wasn't quite right – so much so, in fact, that I voiced my concern to my husband: 'Maybe they found something. Maybe it's cancer.'

My husband did his best to reassure me that everything would be OK, whilst I did my best to put on a brave face, all the while the panic rising inside me.

I spent a sleepless weekend, tossing the 'what if' scenarios around in my head before going to the 'forgotten' appointment on the Monday. My suspicions were raised even further when the receptionist could find no record of the appointment, and then again, when she shared some hushed whispers with her colleague. I was asked to take a seat and then a short time later I was shown to the examination room.

In walked the senior registrar who had performed my surgery, followed by a woman who was introduced to me as the consultant, a woman whom I had never met until that day and who, as it turned out, I would never meet again.

My heart sank and I knew – I knew there and then – the 'big guns' were out. And I was in range. . .

Cancer

As my worst fears became reality, the earth stopped. For a few seconds, I heard nothing. *I can see their lips moving – why can't I hear?* Nothing was registering. I reached for my husband's hand and brought myself back to reality. 'Told you so,' was all I could muster.

I held it together okay for a couple of minutes, until the senior registrar said, 'I'm sorry.' I felt the panic rise like tidal waters. *Oh my God. He thinks I'm going to die.* Then the tears came.

After that I heard the words 'rare', 'aggressive', 'tests'. I heard my husband asking intelligent, scientific questions about statistics and I leapt into action. 'What do we do about it?' I felt I'd screamed the words, yet they were only a whisper.

The Waiting Game

One of the worst things about having cancer is the *waiting*: waiting for an appointment letter to come through the door; waiting in Radiology to go in for a CT scan, all the while drinking that aniseed-flavoured drink they give you by the gallon; waiting for the results of the scan. There is simply nothing anyone can say or do for you during the waiting game that will make much of a difference.

I spent a nervous couple of weeks waiting to have all the tests done, to see if the tiny lesion had managed to dig its claws in anywhere else in my body, then another couple of anxious weeks until I got the results. During this time I got very little sleep – I tossed and turned at night, imagining every possible scenario.

'The cancer hasn't spread.' I registered the words in a state of shock, then the relief washed over me.

'So I don't have cancer any more?'

'You are cancer-free, as far as we can tell. The scan shows no tissue infiltration.'

The Oncologist went on to explain that no treatment was necessary because a) they couldn't see anything to treat, and b) leiomyosarcoma is known to be quite unresponsive to chemotherapy anyway. I was elated, but I had one niggling question: 'Will it come back?'

The Oncologist looked and me and, in typical Kiwi fashion, said, 'I hate to use the word "remission", because that suggests you assume the cancer is going to come back. There is a chance that the disease is already in your bloodstream and unfortunately there are no markers for leiomyosarcoma, but it's highly unlikely in your case.'

My own research into the disease during the waiting period had told me that the five-year disease-free survival rate with my stage and type of cancer was 80 to 90 per cent, and I was determined to be in that group.

I left the hospital on a high. Happy in the knowledge that we had got it in time and thankful once more that I had had the routine operation that had started my cancer journey.

I only returned to the hospital once more before we left New Zealand for good. I had a review meeting with Oncology in November 2008. I felt great: I was completely over my operation, was fitter than I'd been in years, and was asymptomatic, as far as the doctor was concerned. The medical team understandably didn't want to expose me to unnecessary radiation, and so we didn't do another CT scan at that point. It was a decision I was to reflect upon many times further down the line . . .

Tragically, Alex's cancer returned the following year in a highly aggressive form, spreading to her liver and lungs. In June 2009, she received the devastating news from her oncologist that she had multiple inoperable tumours, and could only expect to live for another three to six months. Such however was Alex's indomitable spirit and determination to make every day count that fifteen months later, in August 2010, she was still fighting the disease and jumped at the opportunity to take part in the annual Superdrive Ladies' Charity Challenge. Through her participation in this event, Alex raised £1,600 for Marie Curie Cancer Care, as well as, in her own words, 'having an absolutely brilliant day's craic surrounded by my husband Rich, and my family and friends'.

Alex Lineham
Leiomyosarcoma July 2008 & April 2009

The Lone Duck – Painting by Alex Lineham.

"Fear not I am with you"
Isaiah ch 41 v 10

The Mournes from Murlough by Sam Fox.

In 2008 Ards Borough Council gave permission for an area of land at Kiltonga Wildlife Sanctuary in Newtownards to be used for the creation of a Garden of Reflection.

Tranquility.

Volunteers: day staff from the Housing Executive, Newtownards branch, who gave their time and support in making a difference.

Our youngest volunteer, Charlie Cash.

Charlie's hope: to grow taller than the spade.

Spring bloom.

Peaceful setting.

Full Bloom.

Symbol of hope.

Taking shape.

Picnic benches donated by the charity committee of the ice cream factory, Kiltonga.

Looking good.

Colourful display.

The Rock Pools at the foot of Slieve Donard
(see page 130, second paragraph).

Our Shared Cancer Journey

Written by Phil Gardner
in memory of her daughter Sharonah Gardner

Sharonah, 2008
"Precious memories of
a beautiful daughter."

In memory of my beautiful and precious daughter, Sharonah (18 April 1988 – 23 February 2009).

The story of my cancer journey began long before the word 'cancer' ever entered my everyday vocabulary, or at least had the impact on me that it was eventually destined to have.

It all began back in April 1988 when I gave birth to my second child. The name Sharonah had already been decided on at the seven month stage of my pregnancy, when, after listening to one of my favourite songs on the radio – 'My Sharona' – I received a very definite kick in the belly. I perceived this to be a sign, as my husband and I were in disagreement at the time over our forthcoming baby's name. The name Sharonah was agreed upon and, two months later, she graced us with her presence in the world!

The next 18 years were adventurous, happy and exciting. Sharonah had a big sister, Davina, who was ten-and-a-half years her senior, and a younger sister, Nikita, 18 months her junior. Apart from early childhood mild asthma for Sharonah and Nikita, and a bout of bronchitis for Nikita, I was very content that my girls were otherwise healthy, with no major concerns. All three girls were also intelligent and beautiful – what more could a parent ask for?

For the early years of Sharonah and Nikita's lives we lived happily by the sea. We had our own little enclave, really, with a private beach at the bottom of the garden, where all the children could play safely and contentedly in the sand on the beach. They could be observed from the kitchen window, and whilst I was cooking the family meals, I would put Davina in charge of her two younger sisters – she certainly excelled at being in command! Both Sharonah and Nikita learned to walk on the beach, barefoot. Stumbling on the sand and the odd scrape on their hands and knees were not uncommon. Later on, in their primary years, their time on the beach as children would pay off for these two, with the sturdy, strong legs they had developed there, enabling them to become gymnasts at the tender ages of five and seven. They both particularly excelled as trampolinists, and would in fact continue to compete and achieve at National Level in this very active sport well into their teens. Sporting activities in general would become a major part of all of the girls' lives.

Davina soon moved into her teenage years and became very well settled in her secondary education, getting deeply involved in the school sports which she loved (including hockey), the Duke of Edinburgh Award Scheme and the ATC Cadets, whilst also being an enthusiastic member of the GB. All of these activities became a very important part of Davina's life, with the ATC being the grounding that was to launch her into a career in the Royal Air Force. The two younger girls soon followed in their sister's footsteps and into secondary education too, at Regent House Grammar School in Newtownards.

The years which followed progressed happily, and above all, healthily, and I was more than content with my life and the progress that my children were making in theirs. Davina moved across the water to take up study at university, and kept up her involvement in the Air Force. As ever, Sharonah and Nikita were so proud of their big sister: they always looked up to her.

It seemed like no time before it was Sharonah's turn to hit the university scene, with her younger sister, Nikita, most likely following in her footsteps at the end of her school term. Sharonah's choice of subjects – Tourism and Maths – would be a complete surprise to me! It was now September 2006.

Although I was very happy with the way things were going for my three daughters, and Sharonah was about to realise her dream of commencing university and a new life, much heartache lay within our family circle. A very black cloud hung over us all.

My niece Cathy (my brother Frankie's daughter) was battling cancer, and had been for a number of years. I simply could not fathom how this beautiful young girl (now 24 years of age) should have to cope with such an ugly illness, which had snatched all her dreams and ambitions for the future from her. While striving to cope with her pain and bleak future, she was also of course seeing her many cousins and friends moving on with their lives and achieving their goals. The sadness of Cathy's illness was compounded even more by the fact that she had lost her beautiful sister, Laura, to cancer, 11 years earlier, at the age of 20. Cathy's suffering was long and arduous, and progressively worsened. Whilst Sharonah had been too young to absorb the full extent of her cousin Laura's illness, she was, however, fully aware of and very distressed by Cathy's battle with cancer. This was later to have a very big impact on her own life.

As I have mentioned, I had actually been very surprised at my daughter's choice of course, as well as by her choice of university. Over the years I had perceived my daughter to be someone who preferred to follow the crowd, rather than a leader, and so I was not only surprised, but concerned as to how Sharonah would cope, since she was not to follow any of her friends to their university of choice. This was a revelation in itself to me! She had struck out on her own and nothing could dissuade her from this decision.

Happily, after travelling over to Manchester with Sharonah, her dad and I were relieved to see her settling into her quarters very quickly, and straightaway integrating with the other new students, who had also just arrived with a sense of trepidation and wonderment at this new adventure. I admit I felt a little sad, leaving my daughter behind to start her new life – I also recalled, and reminisced about, having a similarly gut-wrenching feeling with her older sister's university start ten years previously.

Once the university term was underway, I enjoyed (and quite often despaired of!) the knowledge about the antics of the 'Freshers' I gleaned from Sharonah's phone calls and subsequent home visits. I did, however, also savour what I had learned of my daughter's activities at university. As a mother, I had long since grown to accept my children's ways of life since being detached from the apron strings. In fact, I was very proud and secretly accepting of the paths my daughters had chosen in their lives. In particular, I felt exceptionally proud of what Sharonah had begun to achieve, as I truly was not expecting her to cope with the separation from home and friends quite the way that she did. She was settled, had made many new friends, was truly happy with her course, and I was completely content.

But, in February 2007, just five months after Sharonah had started at university, my comfy world was shattered, when the dreaded phone call came from the A&E Department of Manchester Royal Infirmary. Sharonah had collapsed in her Halls of Residence and had been admitted promptly to the Manchester Royal Infirmary. Following blood tests and scans, she had been found to have a brain tumour.

My family and I were so grateful that fate had intervened on the day Sharonah had collapsed in her Halls of Residence. Not one of her flatmates was taking the same degree course as Sharonah, and therefore she would usually go to her various lectures unaccompanied. On that particular fateful morning of 5 February, all the students in the Halls had left the building to attend their lectures. No one was aware that Sharonah was lying in her room, nursing a severe headache and in a state of collapse, with lethargy and blurring of vision. To this day, the full details of what happened next remain unclear. A fellow student flatmate, Dan, unexpectedly returned to the Halls and found Sharonah struggling to remain on her feet: perhaps she heard someone coming into the empty corridor, or she may have been trying to make her way to the bathroom. Dan's prompt attention to the situation quite possibly saved her life that particular morning. He proceeded to contact the other flatmates, and when they all promptly arrived back at the Halls, they realised their friend Sharonah was in a seriously ill state and sought urgent medical attention.

Quite obviously, this was a very daunting and traumatic situation for Sharonah's friends to be faced with. However, they banded together in love and support, and made their way to Manchester Royal Infirmary Casualty Department, where Sharonah had been taken by Emergency Ambulance.

I can barely find the words to describe my feelings that day on hearing this news. Shock, disbelief, fear and horror are but a few of the emotions I can recall. Surely there had to be a mistake – this couldn't be happening to my beautiful, bubbly, fascinating 'Princess Sharonah' (as her great Auntie Anne affectionately called her).

I was advised to get on a plane to Manchester right away. During the course of the conversation on the telephone with the doctor from the

A&E Department, I remarked that, if it was not possible to catch a flight that night, I would endeavour to be on the first flight in the morning – her response was, 'Tomorrow may be too late.' I could barely absorb the meaning of what the doctor was saying – was it possible my daughter might die that night? Thankfully, her father and I were able to secure two seats on the last flight out of Belfast, and we made the anxious and dreaded journey to the hospital from the airport. As at this stage, only Paul (her dad) and I were making our way to Manchester. I arranged for a friend to come and stay with my younger daughter Nikita, who was devastated and in a very distressed state at the news of her beloved sister. I asked Nikita not to inform her older sister, Davina, who worked on the mainland at this stage, until we arrived in Manchester and had learned about the full extent of the illness and the subsequent plan. We were simply not in a position, or a fit state, to answer questions about Sharonah's condition until we arrived at the hospital and spoke to the medical team who were, at this stage, looking after her.

Though weak and in shock from her terrible ordeal earlier in the day, thanks to the very quick thinking of her university friends who had initiated her admission, Sharonah greeted us with a smile and a certain resilience that was totally unique to her.

The hospital had stabilised Sharonah, and, following our arrival in Manchester, she was subsequently transferred to the nearby Neurosurgical Unit. The following day, after various discussions with the hospital doctors, we were more aware of the full extent of Sharonah's condition, and had to begin the heartbreaking task of informing close family and friends. Arrangements were made for Davina and Nikita to join us at the hospital, where we were to be accommodated for the next ten days.

Brain surgery was performed a few days later. In total defiance of what would have been expected post-op, our daughter was up and walking about within hours of her surgery, with no apparent side effects other than the normal post-op ones. Following reports from the neurosurgeon, histopathologist and oncologist, we learned that Sharonah's tumour was malignant and urgent treatment had to be started immediately. The opportunity was offered to her to remain in Manchester for the treatment (radiotherapy and chemotherapy, combined) to be administered at the Yonge Oncology Centre for Young People.

These events had become Sharonah's worst nightmare, and indeed, ours. My daughter detested hospitals, and now she was destined to be attending hospitals as an outpatient, and possibly an inpatient too at times, for the foreseeable future.

A major upset for Sharonah was the fact she was not allowed to wash her hair for at least another week – until the staples in her head could be removed. Due to the nature of the operation, her hair was very matted and bloodied around the scar site. She initially refused to allow her university friends to visit her, as she was distraught and embarrassed at how her hair looked. Thankfully, they were a persistent crew and chose not to be sent away when they came to visit: Sharonah's matted hair was the very least of their concerns. It was hard to believe that, just a day or two after a life-saving operation, Sharonah was enjoying the 'craic' with her university friends, with much laughter drifting through the ward, to the extent that we had to ask them all to keep the noise and laughter down, out of respect to the other very ill patients. What a memory!

The surgical team were amazed at Sharonah's post-op recovery and determination to get out of hospital and get on with her life. We were informed that on, wakening after her operation, the first question Sharonah asked was: 'What does my hair look like – have I got a scar?' This was the source of much amusement to the surgical team, as, in their experience following such a major operation, the patient would usually be more anxious to know how their op went! But then again, we were all reminded that this was a young and beautiful girl whose appearance meant everything to her – especially her lovely, shiny hair, of which she was very proud. She had entrusted her life into the hands of the surgical team to perform their life-saving skills, and hopefully, and very importantly for Sharonah, they had paid attention to her humble request to be careful with her hair. She was just unbelievable!

Tragically, one week post-op, we learned that Sharonah's tumour was Grade IV, malignant and aggressive. Despite being given this most devastating news and being made aware that chemo and radiotherapy were now a certainty, Sharonah had a steely determination to fight back with every ounce of strength she had. And thus the journey and the battle began in earnest.

Although inpatient treatment was offered for the next six weeks in Manchester, Sharonah was adamant that she did not want to stay there, and she suggested that outpatient treatment in Belfast would be more practical and acceptable. This was agreed upon, and the same day we hired a car, and made the gruelling journey to Stranraer for the boat journey home (since Sharonah was unable to fly). En route we had the unenviable task of calling at Sharonah's Halls of Residence to collect some of her personal belongings. A major clear out of her room was scheduled to take place upon her return to Manchester two weeks later for a post-op MRI scan.

The journey to Stranraer was very tiring for Sharonah of course, since she had just been discharged from hospital, with an array and overload of information to absorb regarding her future (so different a future, which two weeks earlier could not have been anticipated), as well as all her various medications. Thankfully, she slept in the back of the car for most of the journey.

I recollect that only once on the boat journey home did Sharonah break down. She was crying and saying, 'Why has this happened to me? I'm too young to have cancer . . . I don't want to die.' She never uttered these words again.

Just a couple of weeks after my daughter had left Hope Hospital in Manchester, we returned to the clinic there for her to have an MRI scan. We drove over this time in an empty jeep, in order to be able to pack up her belongings from her room, and say goodbye to the university life that was now not to be. There was also the heart-breaking task of saying goodbye to all the very good friends she had made in her short stint at university.

Yet again, Sharonah never ceased to amaze me. My heart was breaking for her, wondering how she would cope with packing up and moving out from the place where she had integrated so well, had been so happy and had found her 'niche'. Just a few weeks earlier, she had been planning on moving to a shared house in Fallowfield with her new university friends, for the next term. Her dreams were shattered, but she held her head up high, and accepted that her life and lifestyle had now irrevocably changed. I noted, as we left the Halls, that Sharonah was the only one not crying. She was just so amazingly brave throughout this terrible ordeal.

Back in Northern Ireland, Sharonah returned to her pre-university workplace, part-time, where she entertained all her colleagues, friends and customers with her usual upbeat and humorous antics, denouncing sympathy and self-pity. Within a matter of months, even during chemo sessions, Sharonah pledged to live her life as normally as she possibly could. To this end, her university friends asked if they could come over to Newtownards and visit her. And so, four of her friends came over to stay in the family home for a number of days. The weather was very kind to us and we managed to show them some good old Ulster hospitality. All had a great time, many laughs, and there was some much-needed fun for Sharonah prior to commencing chemo and radiotherapy. For the next year or so, during and post treatment, Sharonah would always bounce back, even taking up a new part-time educational course in the local 'tech': Accounting Technician. Oh, she was so determined. Within a year of commencing this course, she had passed Papers I and II.

Sharonah's resilience, her bubbly nature, love of life, activeness, and sheer determination to live life to the full, inspired everyone who knew her – her family, her many, many friends, her work colleagues and other acquaintances – to take a leaf out of her book and enjoy life as she did. No one would have known, to look at her, exactly what she had gone through, both physically and mentally. This is exactly as she wished – she wanted nothing more than to be 'normal'. After all, she was just a young girl who had had prospects of a bright and happy future ahead of her.

Throughout the year following Sharonah's surgery and treatment, I felt that the dawning of every day brought forth a life-changing experience for me and all of us. Due to my own personal stress and concerns regarding Sharonah's prognosis (of which she herself chose not to be made aware), family life and working life took a dramatic nosedive. Everyday life, as I had always known it, had changed – from a carefree, well-balanced environment and a bright outlook to a life and a future filled with uncertainty. I refused to imagine my life without Sharonah in it – it was just unthinkable. And I couldn't allow her to become aware of my feelings: these had to be suppressed, to ensure normality for my daughter. Sharonah's swift recovery from the operation and continued improvement baffled the medical profession. She believed – since she appeared to have improved beyond belief – that perhaps she had beaten this cancer. There was *hope*.

As Sharonah had lost all of her hair from the site of her craniotomy scar to her forehead, but had suffered no loss of hair to the back of her head, we purchased umpteen soft, broad headbands for her to wear (preferable to her wearing a wig, indeed). Many friends and family began to purchase such headbands for her in an array of colours and designs, and it soon became like a fashion statement for Sharonah to be seen out in so many different brands and styles. Those who were unaware of her illness believed her headbands to simply be fashion accessories that she enjoyed wearing. And of course, as always, she looked terrific in this style, and glowing with health. The loss of some hair was not going to prevent Sharonah from joining her friends on nights out, or continuing to retain her crown as karaoke queen (as she believed herself to rightfully be!), or remaining a vital member of the quiz team. She simply loved her social nights out with her friends.

Even during the course of her chemotherapy treatments, Sharonah planned a holiday to Spain with her friends, in consultation with her oncologist. He was quite happy to work her treatment around her holiday. This proved to be a successful venture!

As Sharonah did not want to put anyone out (even with a change of appointment for blood tests, etc.), she opted to attend the clinic, as usual, on the Monday of that week and booked a flight to Alicante for the Tuesday, hence shortening the holiday to Spain by a few days. (The rest of her friends had their flight booked Saturday to Saturday.) I felt extremely uneasy however, at the thought of Sharonah travelling to Spain on her own (fearing that she might experience sickness, lethargy and maybe panic along the way). Therefore I booked myself on to the same flight, so as to accompany her on the journey. I still laugh at the memory, for Sharonah panicked and believed I was planning on joining her and her friends on their holiday! Indeed, that was very far removed from my actual plan. I just wanted a few days' break on my own, with the comfort of knowing that I would be accompanying my daughter on the flight only to Alicante, and would be in the same country as her, should anything go wrong. I was content in the knowledge that she would be met and looked after very well for the duration by her friends, who were delighted that she was joining them.

Many a humorous, rapid-fire quip emerged from Sharonah's lips – her many friends will testify to that. One such remark stands out: in the course of a conversation in a crowd of friends one time, someone remarked, 'I need this like a hole in the head.' Sharonah's response was simply: 'Duh . . . what's this *I've* got, then?' – making obvious reference to her brain surgery! She never lost her sense of humour throughout her ordeal, always managing to make light of her condition and inject much humour into it.

I also recall hearing of a particular conversation between my niece Cathy and Sharonah, one day when Sharonah and her sister Davina had gone to visit Cathy – who was of course also suffering with cancer – at home. There had been a 'close encounter' along the road for the girls with another driver, and, on relaying this piece of news to Cathy, they had both concluded that it would be a terrible irony if they both managed to come through a harrowing time in their cancer journey, only to be 'taken out' by some 'so and so' in a car accident! I learned that both of them had had a good laugh at that one. It never ceased to amaze me that these young girls, throughout all their suffering and pain, never lost sight of their sense of humour – always a humbling thing to experience. The same could also be said of Cathy's older sister, Laura, also an amazing young lady, whose enthusiasm, determination and love of life had inspired everyone who was fortunate enough to have known her. Tragically Laura lost her battle with cancer back in March 1997, having achieved so much in the few short years since her diagnosis.

Sharonah and Cathy now, sadly, had much in common. Although, following Sharonah's surgery for her brain tumour in February 2007, by all accounts and appearances she made a surprisingly excellent post-op recovery, and preparations had begun for a course of combined chemotherapy/radiotherapy to begin on an outpatient basis. As I have said earlier, until the tragic events of February 2007, Sharonah had never had occasion to be admitted to hospital in her life. In almost 19 years she had been in exceptionally good health, and this was to be a godsend in terms of her ability to recover.

In March 2007, a holiday had been planned for Cathy, her parents and myself, to go to Nice in the South of France: it was to be a special treat for Cathy. Due to the circumstances however, I had to withdraw from this holiday, but very quickly another friend was able to take my place and accompany Cathy and her parents on the trip. Cathy required a lot of assistance in this stage of her journey.

In the week leading up to the departure date for the holiday, the medical staff in the hospice where Cathy was staying at this stage, were very reluctant to release her for the trip, as she was indeed very ill. But so determined was Cathy to make the journey at all costs that she threatened to sign herself out of the hospice, against medical advice, if the doctors did not agree to release her. Sharonah, along with the rest of our family, could not help but admire Cathy's spirit. The family thus went on the holiday, which was to be Cathy's last holiday abroad.

Following Cathy's death in October 2007 – which of course devastated our whole family circle once more – her surviving sister, Tracy, gathered friends and relatives around, and set about organising a charity ball to commemorate and celebrate the lives of her two sisters, Laura and Cathy. The Sunflower Ball was planned for 7 March 2008, in La Mon Hotel, just five months after Cathy's passing.

As this was a fundraising ball, Tracy and her friends very speedily set about the huge task ahead, involving and reeling in fundraisers from every conceivable corner. Indeed, to Tracy and the Ball Committee's credit, the Sunflower Ball proved to be a tremendous success, attracting approximately 650 revellers and raising a tremendous £35,000 for their chosen charity, Marie Curie (the excellent services of which Laura and Cathy had both been able to benefit from).

Sharonah, like the rest of the family, had been eagerly looking forward to this Ball. Gowns were purchased or hired, hair and beauty appointments were made, and great excitement grew as the date of the Ball drew near. Little did I know that in the week of the Ball my daughter was to be struck down with another illness, of unknown origin.

Two days prior to the Ball, Sharonah stayed off work, complaining of severe abdominal pain. As I was absent from the house – on a walking trip on the Causeway Coast – Nikita took the day off school to attend to her sister's needs, as she had become increasingly concerned about the state she was in. As I wasn't there myself, I decided to contact the GP, and requested a home visit. Again, Sharonah's reaction was that I was 'fussing too much'. The GP diagnosed her as being constipated, and gave her a script on this basis. I was hopeful, but very uneasy, about the GP's diagnosis. Two days later, Sharonah felt a slight improvement in her condition and, as always, was determined to go to the Ball. On the night of the Ball she looked fabulous, though in her own unique way she was masking the pain and discomfort that she was in. Photos taken on the night did not highlight what her body was hiding.

Tragically, and suddenly, again, Sharonah showed further signs of illness: this time with stomach pains, anaemia and progressive weight loss, though at the same time brain scans were showing no reactivity in her brain tumour. Another dilemma! Was this a delayed reaction to her chemotherapy, which had finished six months earlier? The suggestion was that this was a reasonable conclusion.

However, throughout this period, Sharonah never missed a day at work, insisting on taking annual leave to attend her hospital appointments, etc. What a stalwart she was. She even mustered up enough energy in July of that year to attend the Oxegen Festival with her sister Davina. The plan was to camp out for a night or two, but after enjoying being entertained by some of the acts at the Festival, Sharonah felt unable to cope with camping out and Davina drove her home again. She did declare that she enjoyed it, nevertheless.

Also this year, one of Sharonah's closest friends, Tara, had asked her to become godmother to her son Ralph. My daughter was elated at the thought of becoming a godmother to this beautiful baby, whom she adored and bragged about frequently. She took such great delight in shopping for outfits for her godson-to-be. I was delighted for her and always noted how uplifting her conversations with Tara seemed to be, and how her face lit up when talking to Tara on the phone to receive frequent updates on Ralph. Tara lived in Sunderland, so I was really pleased for Sharonah when she felt well enough to book a flight and go to visit her friend. The time she spent with Tara and Ralph was clearly very precious and exciting for her. It granted her a much-needed break from the home environment, and for a few days she was overjoyed to have the company of her friend and her 'soon-to-be-godson' to divert from her thoughts of cancer and just be 'normal'. A date was tentatively set for Ralph's christening, and Sharonah's excitement continued to build.

However, as the months passed, various treatments were tried, to build Sharonah up – for example, iron for the anaemia, food supplements when she was unable to tolerate food, and, eventually, and only when I forced the situation, a blood transfusion.

Sadly, however, Sharonah's condition deteriorated so much that admission to hospital was warranted, so that her doctors could determine what was going on. She had been such a fighter, fuelled by determination, that it was practically inconceivable when this admission and subsequent surgery yielded yet another cruel blow, and she was diagnosed with primary bowel cancer (believed to be unrelated to her brain tumour). Having now become so well acquainted with all the terminology to do with brain tumours, I had to familiarise myself with yet another new range of vocabulary. How could this possibly be? We had already all witnessed and suffered the agonising loss of my two nieces to this terrible disease – it was just beyond belief that my family were going through this nightmare again. Many questions were asked, as to why this new problem had not been detected much earlier. Our thoughts went back to the harrowing episodes of pain Sharonah had suffered in March, six months earlier, and the family concluded – and now, it seemed, the surgeons agreed with us – that the signs and symptoms had indeed been present then, but sadly, had not been investigated at the time.

Somehow, myself, my family and all of Sharonah's friends and colleagues managed to 'pull together and rally round' for Sharonah's sake, so that we could help cushion the blow for her when she would come out of the HDU (High Dependency Unit) to learn of yet another devastating diagnosis, with, once again, a very poor prognosis. Just how much more were these young shoulders supposed to bear? I felt sick, to the pit of my stomach, that my precious child, at just 20 years of age, had to endure so much agony. As I looked around me, I observed the pain etched in my family's faces, the despondency again, and the knowledge that the future now looked very bleak indeed. Our lives would never be the same – or as good – again.

True to form for an exceptional young lady, after extensive surgery, Sharonah was discharged from hospital after a mere two weeks, rather than the months predicted by the medics. My daughter faced her destiny with dignity. Yet again, in October 2008, shortly after she had been discharged from hospital, and with daily visits by nurses for medication and practical care, and from family and friends, Sharonah was able to begin a self-teaching course at home for the Accounting Technician Paper III, Not one to sit around and become bored, she was at the same time very much aware she would not be in any fit state to attend a night class to work on this very difficult paper, and so she proceeded to order the necessary book over the Internet and commenced her study. Sharonah remained seriously ill, post surgery, so there was very little opportunity for her to study, except in short bursts in between resting, recuperating and receiving daily visits from the district nurses, in preparation for a new and extensive round of chemotherapy for her bowel cancer. Once again I watched in amazement as my daughter determinedly undertook this new challenge for herself in the middle of everything else she had to cope with. (I was of no help whatsoever, as the topic was far beyond my understanding.)

As post-op recovery was very slow, due to the rapid breakdown in Sharonah's immune system, chemo was restarted somewhat later than planned. As I watched my beautiful girl deteriorating before my eyes, she made an all-out and truly valiant effort to remain bright and cheerful for everyone, in particular when with her very close-knit group of friends. All the while, she masked her pain as only she knew how to.

I recall many, many occasions when just prior to a visit from her friends, Sharonah would have been feeling very poorly, retching and in pain. But, true to form, she would always fix herself up as best she could, put on some make-up, do her hair and greet her friends as they came through the door with her usual loud greeting, as though they hadn't seen each other for a long time. It was simply her way – she did not want her friends to see her in a sickly state. They would surely not have believed how ill Sharonah had been just ten minutes before their arrival. She always made such an effort to look her best for them.

I later learned that Sharonah never discussed her cancer fears or preoccupations with her friends, much beyond a quick update on how her treatment was going. She simply did not dwell on her illness when in the company of her friends, of which there were many. Her preference was simply to enjoy being in their company and delight in the craic and all the news they brought with them. This was the normality of life she wished to hold on to. My daughter did not deserve to be burdened with this tragic illness. But she never showed any signs of self-pity, only her incredible zest for life. I could only observe the coping mechanisms of my daughter with pride and the utmost sadness. With her zany humour, she always somehow managed to put a smile on the faces of her friends and family.

As so much time had to be spent in recovery in the house, I suggested to Sharonah that we take a couple of days away, up at the North Coast, for a change of scenery and she was keen to do this. The Northern Ireland Cancer Fund for Children were able to provide us with accommodation in Pine Cottage, a self-catering holiday home outside Ballymoney (our most heartfelt thanks to this great organisation!). Although we were unable to go for the full week, we still managed to enjoy a nice couple of days in the cottage, relaxing by, for example, watching a couple of comedy DVDs – at times Sharonah laughed so much at these, she was afraid she would burst her wound from the recent surgery! Though she was very weak, we also somehow managed to do some driving around the North Coast, stopping off at various beauty spots: Sharonah took great delight in photographing some of the spectacular scenery, from Castlerock to Ballintoy. One such excellent photo that Sharonah took – of a sandstorm on Castlerock Beach – was later to become the main image on a bookmark memory card I had made up to distributed to her friends and family.

On 3 December 2008, Sharonah dutifully sat Paper III of the Accounting Technician Qualification in Stranmillis College in Belfast.

I recall what a freezing morning it was, with ice glistening on the road. Sharonah had been very, very ill in the week leading up to this, and on the morning of the exam, it took every ounce of strength she had to muster up the energy to leave the house. It was generally felt that she would not be well enough to go through with it, but it had become another distraction for her, so I agreed to drive her to Stranmillis College. Due to the icy conditions and the fact that exam goers had to walk up a steep (and now very slippery) hill to the examination room, I was dismayed when Sharonah refused to let me ask the security officer at the gate if I could drop her off at the main door.

My daughter insisted on me leaving her off in the car park, at the bottom of the hill, where, exhausted and breathless, she proceeded to climb the hill with pride and determination. I sat in my car, with tears streaming down my face, feeling helpless and distraught, as I watched my lovely daughter struggling up the hill, until she was out of sight. I returned two hours later to pick her up (again at the bottom of the hill, at her insistence), then we met with her dad to have a post-exam lunch in Cutter's Wharf. Sharonah made it very clear that we would not be having a post-mortem on the exam, which she declared she had done very badly. After all, she had only had the rare opportunity (over approximately three weeks) to study for the exam, and hadn't managed to get halfway through the book of coursework by the day of the exam.

Regardless of this, we were all extremely proud of Sharonah for what she was trying to achieve despite her very serious illness. But, as if she hadn't suffered enough, the cruelest blow was delivered to my daughter following a chemotherapy session on New Year's Eve 2008. A post-op scan revealed that, yet again, another 'primary' tumour had invaded her body. After this news had been delivered to her, Sharonah broke down, cried, saying to me and her dad, 'I would rather die now, than go through what Cathy went through.' Cathy, her 25-year-old cousin, had passed away in October 2007, having lost her own battle with bowel cancer.

Sharonah had witnessed far too much tragedy in her close family at such a young age, and, at that point, I believe, resigned herself to her inevitable fate. No longer did she have the strength to cling to the hope of a 'miracle'. My own faith was tested to the core, but I simply could not cave in to what had now become a stark reality. Oh, how I prayed for strength to bear the most unbearable burden.

Inspirational as she was however, Sharonah made the decision to celebrate and bring in the New Year with some of her friends. With her PICC line and anti-emetic drips in situ, she was determined that cancer was not permitted on the agenda that night – Sharonah just wanted to party, play, sing and enjoy the company of her friends. She had decided that it was 'gonna be a good night' – a normal, cancer-free night. When she arrived home at 3 a.m., I got my 'Happy New Year' greeting and goodnight kiss from her, along with the declaration: 'That's the best New Year's Eve I've ever had.'

I simply could not absorb what I had just heard from my daughter: once again, I was overwhelmed with pride for her courage. I knew in that instance that it was by pure design, that she had consciously planned, that her last 'night out' with her friends was a night for them all to remember her, just as she always had been in better times. What a wonderful, wonderful girl. And in the final weeks of her life, I would keep discovering qualities in her that were previously unknown to me.

The results of the Paper III exam arrived at the house when Sharonah was in the Intensive Care Unit of the Ulster Hospital, critically ill and basically unresponsive, following further surgery in January 2009. As we, her family, all continued to talk to her every day, it was with tremendous pride but also great sadness that I was able to tell Sharonah that she had achieved 49 per cent in this examination. She just managed to nod her head in acknowledgement. My heart was breaking – I wanted her to scream with delight at how brilliant we all felt she was to have achieved such a tremendous result.

I subsequently contacted the Examining Board and enquired if Sharonah could be granted a few more marks, in light of her serious illness at the time of the examination (50 per cent was the Pass Mark). I was told that she would have been entitled to a mark-up of 5 per cent, had she informed the Board of her critical illness prior to the exam. Sadly however – but also to her credit – she refused to accept any kind of 'sympathy allowance' for her efforts. It remained her aim, to the bitter end, to only receive recognition for what she had actually achieved in life. In my eyes however, and those of her dad, sisters, family and friends, Sharonah had *Passed with Distinction*.

I began to reflect on the things that Sharonah had achieved in the short time since she had first been diagnosed. She always had a big personality, full of fun, quirky and bursting with ideas and plans – but these qualities became even more prominent post-diagnosis.

It is these memories of Sharonah's personality and unique zest for life in spite of all that I cast my mind back to regularly. One scene, which took place during the early stages of her combined radiotherapy/ chemotherapy treatment, stands out in particular. I was escorting my daughter to her radiotherapy appointment at the Belfast City Hospital (this was approximately one hour after she had taken her chemo drugs). Never one to make a scene or draw attention to herself, she was however feeling very sick and started retching violently. She was attempting to rush along the path into the hospital buildings from the car park when we both realised that she wasn't going to make it in time. I encouraged her to just 'let it all go' (and not worry about who would see her, and perhaps think badly of her), so she did . . . into the bushes along the pathway. We joked later about how she had fertilised the bushes and how 'special plants' would probably start to grow there as a result. Many more journeys were made to the Cancer Centre there, and we always had a 'sneaky look' at the bushes, to see if there was anything unusual growing there. It always gave us a laugh.

Another very special memory was the time I took Sharonah for a weekend's respite to Shimna Valley (a holiday home for children living with cancer and their families, set in beautiful surroundings at the foot of the Mourne Mountains). As she was particularly ill this weekend and the weather was beautiful outside, I encouraged my daughter to come for a short drive, in the hope that she could relax a little more whilst I was driving through the Mournes, which might help take her mind off her illness, if only for a short period. As she put the seat back to lie down, off we set through the Mournes, passing hikers and cyclists along the winding roads.

As we travelled deeper into the mountains, I was delighted when, rousing herself from her lethargic state, Sharonah suddenly put her seat up and talked in an excited, gregarious fashion about time she had spent in the Mournes with her friends and schoolmates, when she was struggling to achieve her Duke of Edinburgh's Award. The next couple of hours were full of her reflections and enthusiastic memories of past, fun-filled escapades spent with her close friends in these mountains, in better times. It was an amazing journey. On the return drive to Shimna Valley, Sharonah demanded that we stop at the Bloody Bridge, along the coast road, just on the outskirts of Newcastle, and walk up the path to the rock pools there, which she described as 'one of my most favourite places on earth'. I dreaded this journey, as I felt she was too weak to tackle the uphill walk over such rocky terrain. How wrong was I? I actually had trouble keeping up with her, much to her amusement!

On arrival at the rock pools, the most beautiful sight met our eyes, as the sun, perching in all its glory on top of Slieve Donard, reflected off the water and the rocks, sending hundreds of rays beaming down on us. I captured this vision – like a universe in its entirety – in a number of breathtaking photographs. In one of these pictures, Sharonah is taking a photo of herself on her mobile phone, sitting amongst the rocks which she had climbed onto, beside the cascading waterfalls. She had suggested that it would be too dangerous for me to climb down over the rocks to where she was sitting, and so, reluctantly at first, I stayed put on dry ground. It soon became apparent to me that my daughter wanted this precious and contemplative time to be alone with her own thoughts. There and then I logged the memory of that scene into my own memory bank, where it will remain with me for the rest of my days.

For years, I had tried to encourage all of my daughters to appreciate the beauty of their surroundings, but sensed, until this memorable day with Sharonah, that I had somehow failed. Though I suspected that I had failed my child in many ways, as I was unable to do enough to save her from her fate, in time, many, many months later, after her death, I learned to accept that I wasn't to blame for my daughter's cancer. Slowly, through time, I have learned to let go of the bad feelings that have haunted me since the onset of my daughter's illness.

Towards the end of 2007, on completion of Sharonah's treatment for her brain tumour and after the very sad and tragic death of my niece Cathy, I found myself drawn to an opportunity to take up a course in Cancer Support. Whilst during the initial interview stage with my potential tutor, it was suggested more than once that the timing for undertaking such a course was perhaps not very appropriate for me, I managed to convince my tutor-to-be that the timing was not inappropriate at all, but essentially perfect, in fact. As a student on the Cancer Support course, I had an obligation to interact and involve myself with, and help and support, people living with cancer. This involvement led me to the HOPE Cancer Support Group. A new journey in a new environment had begun.

Though I had joined the HOPE Cancer Support Group primarily as an aide and comforter for its members, I found myself being drawn into their warmth and friendliness and subsequently experienced a personal need to 'belong' to this extraordinary group of people, who, in the long-term, would unexpectedly become my 'alternative family' in my time of crisis. I would find myself entering into a situation of role reversal and becoming the recipient of a huge outpouring of love and understanding. Strange as it may seem now, it was initially very confusing for me, as this was not the role I was supposed to be playing. Due to my eventual loss, which was so personal and devastating to me, I gained unbelievable comfort from the members of the Group, who, I felt, should have been concentrating more on their own problems and difficulties arising from their own cancer journeys. Yet they had so much to give me – it was such a humbling experience.

Even from the beginning of my involvement, many individual, heartbreaking stories emerged from within the Group. In particular, I became fascinated with a new member, Alex, who had just been given a devastating cancer diagnosis, but who set about defying the odds, living life to the full and challenging everything that lay ahead, always with a determination and positive attitude that this cancer could be beaten. I was so impressed by Alex's bravery that I requested an interview with her as part of my coursework in the Cancer Support Course I was in the process of completing. Alex was my 'Case Study' for a very important element of the course, and it is thanks to her very generous input as well as my own efforts that, I am proud to say, I passed the module in question.

The completion of another module of the course had to be postponed twice, due to Sharonah's critical illness. Once she was out of immediate danger again – following life-saving surgery, an unexpected transfer to the surgical ward, and a couple of days in the High Dependency Unit – I was once again encouraged by those around me to take some 'time out' from the hospital and return to my course. The module in question was being taught over a two-day period, and Sharonah gave me her blessing too: I should definitely go. It was a welcome relief from the intensity of the hospital setting, and an opportunity too for other family members and her many friends to rotate visits with Sharonah. I was very much aware too that the skills I was learning on the course would be useful and practical for me, following Sharonah's imminent discharge from hospital.

Throughout this module, and indeed the course as a whole, I drew comfort and understanding from the course group, as well as both practical and emotional support. It was comforting being able to share the traumas, fears and experiences with such a close-knit group, who had also become like a second family to me. It was thus during this period of study that I was able to develop a much deeper understanding of some of the feelings a person living with cancer may be going through. Whilst my daughter never actually fully engaged in conversation about the possibility of dying as a result of her illness, she did intimate her awareness of this, albeit by skirting around the issue.

One particular example of this occurred after Sharonah's surgery in September 2008, while we were sitting around the dinner table. The conversation related to the fact that all of her friends were due to celebrate their 21st birthdays in the months which followed. Sharonah asked if I would do her a favour, and ensure that everyone celebrated her 21st birthday (which was to be on 18 April 2009). She specifically mentioned one of her very close friends, Janet, who was completing part of her degree course in the South of France. She said that Janet was always broke and was worried that she would not be able to afford the airfare home to celebrate her birthday. (The majority of Sharonah's friends either lived close by or were students in Scotland or England, and so would not encounter the same difficulties transport-wise.)

I responded by saying that she could organise all this herself, but I was faced with a stern glare and a grave response from my daughter: 'Please Mum, promise me you will all celebrate my 21st birthday, even though I won't be there.' It was impressed upon me that I had to ensure Janet's return from France, with Sharonah insisting that she would pay for her friend's flight. 'I've got money in the bank and won't get a chance to use it,' she said.

It then registered with me, exactly what Sharonah was saying, and when I attempted to lighten the mood, she looked me straight in the eye, with a fixed stare, and said, 'Please Mum, promise me – I won't be here – you know what I mean.' Naturally, I made the promise, with a broken heart, then excused myself and turned away, on the pretext of making a cup of tea. I could no longer look my daughter in the eye and found myself silently sobbing, with tears flowing down my face. But I could not allow my daughter to see me break down. My courage was waning, whilst I observed that Sharonah's was strengthening.

In January/February 2009, when I was due to complete the final module of my CSC course, heartbreakingly, Sharonah was once again admitted to hospital. This was to be the final stage of her cancer journey.

The outpouring of love for Sharonah was overwhelming. Throughout her time in HDU/ICU, all of her friends – most of whom were in placements at various universities across the water – travelled home and gathered in the hospital to lend their support and love to their beloved friend. Due to the seriousness of Sharonah's condition, they were unable to visit her, but they wanted to be together to share and comfort one another and their friend's family at this very critical time. They were all a part of her, and she a vital part of them – this 'alternative family' of friends, who had spent so much of their lives together since uniting and forming the closest of bonds since their first year of secondary education. The very special bond between them all was never broken, even when they were destined to study at different universities. They had Bebo, texting, mobile phones and Facebook to help them keep in touch with each other on a daily basis. Their lives were inextricably bonded, and I reflect and am proud to this day that my daughter was an 'unbreakable' link in the chain of such a great bunch of friends – more commonly known as 'Team Cheese'!

Whilst sitting around Sharonah's hospital bed, we – her dad, myself, her older sister and her younger sister – silently and with immense grief had no choice but to acknowledge that our lives had changed irrevocably, that our future was compromised and our trust in the world denied. The price for love is grief. Yet . . . we had to let go. Memories never die, and death is not a conclusion – a sequel lies beyond.

At the news of Sharonah's passing, on 23 February 2009, so many people remained numbed and shocked, as intense prayers for her recovery were being said all around the country, and beyond. But it was not to be. The very daunting task of preparing for her funeral began.

My family and I were overwhelmed by the masses of people who visited our home over the next couple of days, and who packed the church to capacity to pay their respects to this wonderful young lady, whose life was taken from us much, much too soon. Nor had she been forgotten by the university friends she had made in the very short time she had spent there: seven of these friends whom she hadn't seen in over 18 months travelled over here from Manchester, stunned and sorrowful, to pay their respects at her funeral and link up with all the other wonderful friends with whom she had shared her life. Many funny stories were exchanged at this gathering about our wonderful daughter, more commonly known among her friends as 'Sharonah Corona' or 'Shaz'.

Following the service all Sharonah's friends and her family gathered together in Roma's, where she herself had enjoyed many nights out. She was once again honoured and paid tribute to, when a musician friend played his guitar and sang her favourite song: Snow Patrol's 'Run'. It was a very moving moment and my daughter's spiritual presence was very much felt at this gathering.

In the days, weeks and months following Sharonah's passing, not a single day passed but that her name wasn't mentioned – so many people that she knew each had a special memory to share, that was unique to their friendship or acquaintance with her. My life, and the lives of my family, family circle, my friends, my family's friends, and in particular,

Sharonah's friends and all who knew her – all have been enriched by knowing her and having had her in their lives.

Not too many months later, I kept my promise to Sharonah, and on 18 April 2009 (Sharonah's 21st birthday), 15 of her closest friends returned to Newtownards, from their various universities and places of work, to join the family in a special celebratory dinner to honour the beautiful memories we individually, and as a group, shared of such a wonderful and brave young woman. Just eight weeks after she had passed away, this night was a celebration of her wonderful life. There were no tears around the dinner table: just stories, laughter and fellowship.

Many dreams have been dreamt since, dreams of such vividness, that on awakening, it really has seemed unbelievable that the whole scenario was indeed just a dream, so different from the reality that myself and my loved ones have to continue struggling to come to terms with on a daily basis. The dreams that I have had about my daughter have shaken me to the core. I then begin to doubt myself and begin to wonder: 'am I losing my mind?' My dreams are always beautiful and so real that I subsequently understand that this is how I wish it was, in real time!

In the weeks and months following Sharonah's passing, myself and my family were literally smothered with love and caring, both in the form of emotional support and practical gestures, from family, friends and colleagues, who simply could not do enough for us in our grief-stricken state. Aside from the many people already mentioned who were part of Sharonah's life, her beloved 'Granny' was simply heartbroken beyond belief. Having lived to four times Sharonah's age, she kept questioning how and why such a young life could be taken by this terrible disease, when she herself had on so many occasions overcome life-threatening illnesses.

The many people whom I have met throughout my daughter's illness and subsequent death have provided me with such an insight into life, past and present, that my whole being and attitude has changed dramatically.

Each and every day now, I reflect on what my life was like before cancer – when everyday living was exciting and adventurous, with absorbing news from family and friends, particularly of course that relating to the lives of my three children, whose sense of adventure and zest for life excited me the most. My life today – more than ever before – has become a life full of reflection. Whilst my daughter was still alive and living through her cancer treatment, there seemed so little time or energy for reflection – time seemed to be more creatively and productively spent researching, enquiring, planning and hoping for successful outcomes. Where would we be without our faith and hope?

Now, in the present, every day still remains a continuous learning curve. Without a particular focus, I had harboured many myths and misconceptions about the many different forms of cancer and how they may have arisen. Throughout my daughter's illness, I became more focused on what facts we have about how these cancers can develop and indeed how this terrible illness was brought to my family. I could no longer ignore it – it had become personal, very, very personal. I subsequently had to learn to develop a coping strategy. I'm still learning this today.

In my many troubled days and months following my daughter's death, I experienced such heartbreak and sadness, bordering on depression, that I simply believed the pain would never heal. In these times, when I felt so low and despairing, I had the experience more than once of encountering white feathers inexplicably floating down and dropping at my feet. These feathers became symbolic to me, as I started to believe they appeared each time as a message to uplift me. When, however, I looked for them and consciously wished for them, they didn't appear: this would only ever happen to me quite unexpectedly, in the most unusual circumstances. I have since Sharonah's death experienced quite a number of other 'strange' phenomena.

It seemed somewhat ironic to me that, just a little over a week before the first anniversary of Sharonah's death, the writer of the song 'My Sharona' died of cancer himself. I gathered up all the articles which appeared in the papers about this singer/songwriter, and was fascinated to see, for the first time, a photograph of the 'original' Sharona, about whom the song was written. I couldn't help but smile and wonder what my own Sharonah would have made of it all – and I pictured her hovering above. Since then, the song has been played often on the radio and used in TV and cinema adverts. It has been described over the years as a 'One Hit Wonder' – and I often make the comparison with my very own Sharonah, who was most definitely a 'One Hit Wonder' too.

Whilst raising my family, I never in my wildest imagination could have suspected what lay ahead for me – that the happiness I've known through bringing up my three children ('my girls') would give way to the sadness and heartbreak I had come to know through losing one of them, and the apprehensions I now have for my two remaining girls, whose future health and happiness mean the world to me. They have such a heavy cross to bear on their journey through life without their sister. But, I also like to remind them, as I am reminded myself, that their lives, and mine, have been so enriched to have had such a wonderful sister and daughter in Sharonah.

Throughout this harrowing and constant grieving period in my life, I have been fully supported by my very close friends, work colleagues and family; in particular, my four sisters. I really cannot thank my family and friends enough for all the love and support they have given me.

But now, another cancer journey has begun in the family. My beloved sister, Angela, who has been a rock to me throughout Sharonah's cancer journey and beyond, has recently been diagnosed with breast cancer and is currently undergoing treatment herself. Angela is now faced with her own set of challenges in undertaking her own 'Journey of Hope'.

With the love and support of our wide family circle, we have once again joined forces, and the 'Family Army' has gone into battle again.

'Oh, My Little Pretty One . . .'

You Will Never Be Forgotten, Sharonah.

Phil Gardner
For **Sharonah Gardner**
Brain Tumour, February 2007
Bowel Cancer, September 2008

The Difference God Makes

Eleanor Whitcroft
Colorectal Cancer, 2000

Monday, 7 February 2000

The day had come for the results of my tests. I went off feeling positive, not nervous about the outcome. What a shock, however – not what I expected at all. All the X-rays were normal but the ulcer that had been removed showed abnormal cells: cancer – that awful word. I couldn't believe it. So many questions. So many doubts and fears. How would I cope? How could I tell the family? Somehow that day, I managed to drive home.

The first people I phoned were my husband and my daughter. It was devastating for us all. My sister was next on the list. I only coped that day through her love and support. Next, my two sons had to be told – my heart was breaking for them all. Eventually all the family were told.

My first reaction after telling my husband was tremendous anger. How could God do this to me? *Why, God? Why?* This was my worst nightmare come true. The next day, I was to speak to the surgeon at Bangor Hospital.

Tuesday, 8 February 2000

I spoke to the surgeon, Mr Campbell. Another examination – no punches pulled here: nothing positive to cling to. Next step, surgery, with a scan first, then radiotherapy for one week before the big op.

That afternoon, I knew I had to speak to Alan, my minister. Now was the time I needed God in my life more than ever. How could I ask Him to help me? I had been so angry with Him. The first thing I had to do was make my peace with Him before I could ask for His healing touch. Alan arrived straight away. He listened to me through the tears. Once Alan prayed with me, I felt more at peace and with a lot more strength to begin to face up to the problem.

Wednesday, 9 February 2000

Another day: more tears, more uncertainty, more fears. *God, help me.* How can I go on? Not knowing, fearful of the scan results and pending operation. Somehow another day passed – tears, tears and more tears.

Thursday, 10 February 2000

Trying to keep cheerful and do the usual day-to-day things. With my husband's support and love, I am coping (only just). I am finding it hard to spend time in prayer. Once I get around to reading God's word for the day, my spirits are lifted.

> Philippians 1:2: 'Grace be unto you.'
> 2 Corinthians 12:9: 'My grace is all you need. My strength comes into its own in your weakness.'

When does grace come? When you need it most. We will find grace to help us when we need it: Hebrews 4:16: 'God will not give you tomorrow's grace today, but when you wake in the morning, it will be there – grace, equal to every need.'

You'll either find a solution to the problem or the grace to handle it, learn from it and come out stronger (see 'Grace be unto you', *Word for Today* (United Christian Broadcasters, 2000)).

Friday, 11 February 2000

Once again God's words of comfort for another day: regardless of the path you walk, never forget that, 'It is God which worketh in you' (Philippians 2:13).

What a comfort, what a wonderful God I have! My best day so far this week. After my daily readings, God once again lifted me up. If we allow the resurrecting power of Christ to operate in our life when we fall into discouragement, God will enable us to stand in the midst of contrary winds. When you stumble, grasp the hand of His grace and get right back up again – they that stumble are girded with strength. If you are about to break beneath the weight of your struggles, be relentless. Don't give up on your family; don't give up on yourself. (See *Daily Notes*). Get up – for by God's grace, you're going to make it.

Saturday, 12 February 2000

Feeling down again. Had another weep, again feeling unsure. Once again, needed to feel the comfort of God's grace.

Sunday, 13 February 2000

Another weepy morning, feeling uncertain again, needing lots of support from John. After spending some time in prayer, felt at peace once again. Words of comfort for today: Psalm 118:14: 'I will not die, but live and proclaim what the Lord has done'.

Is this what God intends for me? Perhaps for me to share with others just what He has done and is doing in my life? As today draws to a close, John and I have a more positive outlook – best day so far. What will tomorrow bring? Scan day and a visit to the stoma nurse.

Prayer for tomorrow:

God give us Your strength and courage to face the new day.

Monday, 14 February 2000

Met with the stoma nurse and was weepy yet again (how I hate feeling like this). After a chat with the nurse however, I left feeling a bit more positive and hopeful. The cancer is not a fast-growing one and scans are done routinely to check the liver, etc.

Had the CT scan – not as bad as I expected. Was also given a video and booklets on the stoma. I was very upset by the video tape, yet it gave me hope that I too could lead a normal life afterwards. It would be a long hard road and a good, positive outlook would be needed.

Somehow today I found it difficult to pray and was not even receptive to God's Word as I did my daily reading. I felt disappointed in myself. I know God is still there watching over me but sometimes negative thoughts are foremost in my mind. I felt I had quite a bad day emotionally.

Tuesday, 15 February 2000

Another day of waiting, not knowing. I spent time in prayer with the Lord and found a calm. Once again, I cling to the words in Psalm 117:17: 'I will not die but live and proclaim what the Lord has done.' I have tried to fully commit this situation into God's hands. I have asked for healing and a renewing of His spirit, strength and courage for this new day.

This verse was on a card from my friend Jenny today: more encouragement to face yet another day: (Psalm 62:8): 'Trust in Him at all times.'

Wednesday, 16 February 2000

Feeling a lot more at peace today. Had my time of prayer, once again committing the situation into God's hands. Thanks be to God for His peace.

My reading for today speaks of grief and trials – even through this, I give God praise for His sustaining strength: 1 Peter 1: 6-8: 'The glory and honour are His, not mine, without Him I am nothing. He gives me the courage to face each new day.'

Alan called today. Thank God for Alan, for his loving care and compassion.

Thursday, 17 February 2000

Awoke early today – 6 a.m. Spent time in prayer, thanking God for the strength and grace for another day. Before sleeping last night, felt fearful again. Talked to God about it, fell into a peaceful sleep.

My reading today, 'When Trouble Works for Us' (*Our Daily Bread* (RBC Ministries, Lancs, 2000)), expressed my feelings exactly. When we feel all is against us, we know we are supposed to trust God and when we find it hard to understand why our circumstances are so difficult, as God says in 2 Corinthians 17: 'Our light affliction, which is but for a moment, is working for us a far more exceeding eternal weight of glory.' We think our afflictions are working against us, but God says they are working for us. They're producing a glory that will last forever. Compared to our trials, the glory is always greater – so don't lose heart.

From God's perspective our trials are 'but a moment'. We can trust the word of a kind and loving Father. God can use things that seem to be against us and cause them to work for us. By faith, we can embrace His perspective today. I found this reading for today very encouraging. Each day, I look for God's message in His word.

Thank you, God, for this new day.

Friday, 18 February 2000

Awake very early again today, had my quiet time in prayer and reading God's word. Reading today about our uniqueness. God loves us, no matter how we look, even with all our faults and failings. He is there for us, even in times of weakness. Psalm 139 talks of how God knows when we sit or rise. He knows our every thought. He knew us when we were being formed in our mother's womb.

Praise God – there is none like Him.

Saturday, 19 February 2000

Didn't sleep too well last night. I worried a lot about the operation and whether or not all would be well. I know it is all in God's hands and I have to keep trusting in Him and in the power of prayer from both family and friends and my church. Felt a bit weepy again, but as the day went on, God once again gave me the strength and courage to face the day.

Sunday, 20 February 2000

Went to church today – worried about how I would cope, but once again God's grace carried me through. Felt really happy and uplifted by the praise. Came away feeling very much at peace.

I love the following words, from a book by Helen Steiner Rice, *Fragrance of Hope*:

It's Me Again, Lord
Remember me, God?
I come every day
Just to talk with You, Lord,
And learn how to pray.
You make me feel welcome,
You reach out Your hand,
I need never explain
For You understand.
I come to You frightened
And burdened with care
So lonely and lost
And so filled with despair,
And suddenly, Lord,

I'm no longer afraid
My burden is lighter
And the dark shadows fade
O God, what a comfort
To know that You care
And to know when I seek You
You will always be there.

Monday, 21 February 2000

Felt pretty good today, although at times felt weepy too. Went to my daughter's home for tea, and returned around 8.15 p.m. Spent time doing my daily reading, felt very alone, tears flowed. Trying not to think of what I have yet to face. *I don't want to die, God.*

'Not my will, but Yours': these are very hard words to say and mean. I hate to think of my family alone – what a very frightening thought. More tears. But God knows how I really feel, even before I speak to Him.

Tuesday, 22 February 2000

Had a better day. Thank God for getting me through another day. Visit to Oncology department tomorrow.

Wednesday, 23 February 2000

Feeling nervy – hospital appointment at 11.30 a.m. Praying for the strength and courage to face visit.
Psalm 55: 22: 'Cast your cares on the Lord and he will sustain you.'
This is a heavy burden for us all. May the Lord give us strength for each new day.

Thank you, Lord, for a loving family.

Have a more positive outlook today after seeing Dr Henry – praise God for His mercies and my answered prayers.

Thursday, 24 February 2000

Bible reading for today is Deuteronomy 1:26 -33 – a very encouraging passage entitled 'Carry Me'. The Lord can carry us and all our burdens and cares, even when we are afraid – He will lift us up and carry us along, no matter how frightened we may be. Our heavenly Father will see us through: '*With God's arms beneath us, we need not fear what lies before us.*' These are words of comfort as I face the next step. Belvoir tomorrow, for planning of treatment. In God's strength, I will find the grace to cope.

Friday, 25 February 2000

Once again, God's peace and love have helped me cope with my visit to Belvoir this a.m. I came away feeling a great peace, now that things are finally moving.

Radiotherapy begins on Monday, 6 March. The operation is on the following Monday. One step at a time. God gives me grace for each new day. Sitting in Belvoir today made me realise just how many people have many fears, just as I have. I only pray that they too will know God's peace and love.

Psalm 39:5 – life is 'but a breath'. Only when faced with a life-threatening illness does this verse become a reality for us all, but:

'The Lord is a stronghold in time of trouble and my hope is in Him alone.

All through the storm the Lord is there.'

Psalm 34:8: 'Taste and see that the Lord is good blessed is the man who takes refuge in him.'

Saturday, 26 February 2000

Felt a bit down today: tears were never too far away, but with God's help I got through another day. Went out with friends for a meal. Enjoyed the evening, but came home very tired. Thanked God for the end of another day.

Sunday, 27 February 2000

Feeling quite good this morning – going to church with my daughter. I know that without God's strength bearing me up, I would be unable to face it. Need to feel God's loving touch and peace within.

Monday, 28 February 2000

Feeling quite good today. Met with Eva, who has been through the same operation. We got on well together. Eva is a Christian, so it was easy to talk to her. I really felt that the Lord had brought us together. She helped me and we both agreed that it is only through the Lord's strength that we can cope. God helps us to face the challenges of each new day. He gives us the courage when we draw strength from Him. 'To trust is to triumph for the battle is the Lord's.' (From *Our Daily Bread* (see above))

Tuesday, 29 February 2000

Good day today, although a bit down in the afternoon. Spent time with the Lord, praying and reading his word. Felt at peace once again, and opened my bible at Psalm 117:17. I felt once again that this was God's word for me: 'I will proclaim what the Lord has done for me.'

Wednesday, 1 March 2000

A bit down this morning, but the words, 'Be bold, Be strong, for the Lord your God is with you', kept coming to mind. What a wonderful God! When we reach out in our distress, he is there: he knows all our anxious thoughts.

Psalm 37:5 'Commit your way to the Lord and trust in Him.'

Psalm 37:39: 'He is their stronghold in times of trouble.'

The Lord is my rock, without Him it would be impossible to face each day. Only through His grace and strength can I cope.

Thursday, 2 March 2000

Feeling good today – with God's strength I will get through another day.

Psalm 42 v 5: 'Put your hope in God.'

Even when we feel down we can trust a loving saviour to carry us through. He can take the burden when it gets too heavy to carry.

Friday, 3 March 2000

Psalm 46:10: 'Be still and know that I am God.'

Awake early today – 5 a.m. This is the best time of the day for prayer, when all is quiet. No interruptions – it is good to spend time in quietness and stillness before the Lord.

Psalm 46:11: 'The Lord Almighty is with us: the God of Jacob is our fortress.'

How apt these words are for me – without God as my fortress, it would not be easy to face each new day. He renews my strength day by day. He is with me now and will be there for me and the family in the days ahead.

Psalm 48:1: 'Great is the Lord and most worthy of praise.'

Afternoon – very weepy, feeling down again. Alan my minister called – strange how Alan turns up on my 'down' days. God knows my need to find peace. I believe He sends Alan just when I need prayer. *Thank you Lord.*

Saturday, 4 March 2000

Feeling not too bad in the morning, although tears were not far away. Sometimes even with people all around, I feel very lonely and lost, angry even. I know God is there but yet sometimes I feel far away from Him; He is right by my side, but I don't reach out – why? Is it my human nature, perhaps thinking I can cope alone?

Feeling a bit weepy again in the afternoon. Spent time in God's presence reading His word.

Psalm 50:15 'Call upon me in the day of trouble, I will deliver you, and you will honour me.'

More words of reassurance – thank you, God. My prayer is to honour you all the days of my life. I give you all the glory for this time: without your strength and ever-loving arms, life would be unbearable. I commit to you the week ahead, when radiotherapy begins.

Sunday, 5 March 2000

Thank God for this new day. By the renewing of His strength, I can face another day. Went to church today, had communion, felt God's peace. At times today, tears were close, especially when thinking that the time for my operation is drawing closer.

Radiotherapy tomorrow, again the Lord will give me strength to see this week through.

Psalm 55:22-23: 'Cast your cares on the Lord and he will sustain you. But as for me, I trust in you.'

Monday, 6 March 2000

Radiotherapy today. All went well. Felt calm and at peace. Thank God for all the prayers being said for me.

Joshua 1:9: 'Be strong and courageous. Do not be terrified, do not be discouraged, for the Lord your God will be with you wherever you go.'

1 Peter 5:10: 'The God of all grace . . . will himself restore you and make you strong, firm and steadfast.'

These words of encouragement are from a leaflet entitled, 'When I am Afraid'. There have been many times when I have been afraid, but God's words bring comfort and peace.

Tuesday, 7 March 2000

Therapy again this morning. Feeling ok about the treatments – two down, three to go. God's word for today:

Psalm 56 v 11: 'In God I trust, I will not be afraid.'

As I face surgery next week, I need His strength to sustain me and see me through what lies ahead. I am trusting in His healing power.

Wednesday, 8 March 2000

Felt a bit down today, a bit weepy at times, but managed with God's help to get through another day. Felt a little brighter in the afternoon

Thursday, 9 March 2000

Morning – treatment again. Felt a bit sick first thing. This improved as the day went on. Met a friend today: she too will be praying for me. What a great thing prayer is. I know that without all the prayers being said on my behalf, I could not cope.

Over the next few days I will need God's strength to face Monday. *He is my strength, without Him, I am nothing.*

Romans 8:26: 'The Spirit helps us in our weakness, the Spirit Himself intercedes for us.'

Psalm 59:16: 'You are my fortress, my refuge in times of trouble.'

Friday, 10 March 2000

Awake early today. Spent time in prayer and reading God's word. Feel very much at peace this morning.

Psalm 62:8: 'Trust in Him at all times, pour out your heart to Him, for God is our refuge.'

I thank God that I can come to Him with all my worries and fears, and He will calm me. Last day of radiotherapy today.

Saturday, 11 March 2000

Cramps quite bad early on, but these eased off as the morning went on. Prayed for God's strength to see me through another day. The words, 'Be bold, be strong, for the Lord your God is with you' are very prominent in my thoughts.

Psalm 68: 9: 'Praise be to the Lord, to our God our Saviour, who daily bears our burdens.'

This has certainly been a heavy burden to bear, not just for myself but for my husband and the family as well – but thank God, He is able to carry it for us all.

Without the prayers of family, friends and church, it would just be too much to bear. Really feel that through all the prayers, God has given and will give me the grace to see it through.

Praise be to God, bless His holy name.

Sunday, 12 March 2000

Going into hospital today, feeling very nervous. Spent time in prayer, asked for God's peace and courage to get me through the day.

Hebrews 13:5-6: 'Never will I leave you; never will I forsake you, the Lord is my helper.'

1 Peter 5:10: 'The God of all grace will himself restore you and make you strong, firm and steadfast.'

6 p.m.: Feeling quite at peace now. I have seen the houseman and had a chat about operation and what is going to happen. No food! (I'm starving.) 8 p.m.: Bowel preparation Operation tomorrow afternoon. In the evening, I remember God's words: 'I am the one who strengthens you.' I just pray He will give me peace tonight and that I will sleep well in preparation for tomorrow.

Monday, 13 March 2000

The longest day of my life. Nothing to drink for a day and a half. I thought

I would die. Once again, Alan called in my time of need and prayed with me. I felt very much at peace – I just committed the whole situation to the Lord and asked for His healing touch. All went well. I was back in recovery before I knew it.

Tuesday, 14 March 2000
Very tired, but felt really good. In fact, I felt as if I hadn't had an operation, apart from the stitches and stiffness. Once again, I committed the whole situation to the Lord and praised Him for His healing touch. God is so good. He has brought us through this ordeal.

Wednesday, 15 March 2000
Feeling a lot better today. I was given a unit of blood. Felt very agitated in the afternoon however, and a bit sorry for myself. I spent a lot of time in prayer and felt a real warmth from the Lord's healing touch.

Praise God for His great mercies and His healing touch in my life. Thank you, God.

Thursday, 16 March 2000
Walked today – the first time since the operation. Very tired by end of the day. Praise God for His strength.

Friday, 17 March 2000
Another new day – feeling quite good this morning. Had catheter removed first thing: one more drain to go. Hoping to be a bit more mobile today and have a shower, etc.

God is doing wonderful things. When I look around and see so many tragic cases coming into hospital and see their lives restored, I realise what a wonderful God we have.

Perhaps there will be days of frustration ahead, getting used to a new way of life. But whether I am frustrated or contented, God is always there. I know I still have to face the pathology report but the outcome is in God's hands. Of course I don't want any more treatments and so on, but whatever the outcome, I know God in His mercy will heal me.

Saturday, 18 March 2000

Didn't get much sleep last night – the ward was quite noisy. I felt very sore and tired, but stronger as the day went on. Spoke to Mr Campbell today: he is happy with my progress. Walked a bit more, but I am very easily tired.

Sunday, 19 March 2000

Feeling a bit more flexible today, although a few cramps.

Monday, 20 March 2000

Bad news again – Pathology tests show two glands may still be affected. Once again I feel angry, or maybe just numb. I feel let down – how could God let this happen? Life is tough!

Alan called just when I felt most alone – yet again, he prayed with me and left me feeling a sense of peace. Still feel weepy though – must continue in a positive attitude. My concerns are for my husband and family. Once again it breaks my heart to have to tell them. *God help me! We all need Your strength and courage to see us through another difficult time.*

Jeremiah 29:12: 'Then you will call upon me and come and pray to me and I will listen to you. You will seek me and find me when you seek me with all your heart.'

Tuesday, 21 March 2000

Isaiah 40:31: 'They that wait on the Lord shall renew their strength; they shall mount up with wings as eagles; they shall run and not be weary; they shall walk and not faint.'

I talked with the stoma nurse today. The treatment not as hopeless as I had thought. Praise God!

Wednesday, 22 March 2000

Feeling more positive today. *Rejoice in the Lord always.* I do rejoice that God has brought me this far. With His help, I will once again regain my positive attitude.

Philippians 4:5-6: 'The Lord is near. Do not be anxious about anything, but in everything by prayer and petition with thanksgiving, present your requests to God.'

God will meet all my needs. I know I still have six months of chemotherapy to face but with God's help and strength, I will cope.

From the book, *The Difference God Makes* by Peter Haile (Worldwide, 1987), I have taken this extract which I feel applies to me, where the author talks about God taking men and women up to and beyond what seems to be the limit of their endurance:

Is it because as far as God is concerned, there's just one ultimate good for humanity, and that is not contentedness and peace. The only good is absolute trust and dependence on Him, and this can only be achieved by our being brought time and again to the end, the real end, of our human resources. We should trust Him and love Him.

Time and again we do not take God at His word until we are desperate and all human hope is exhausted. Time and again, we like to try to keep some human expedient in reserve, just in case Jesus doesn't come through. So Jesus, because he loves us, does not hurry to our rescue. He has to make sure that all human hope is finished.

God cannot accept a little bit of faith in Him. His plan is death and then life – Death to ourselves and then life in Him.

Death for Life
Unless we are willing to go the whole way with Jesus Christ – the way of death to our cherished ideas of what is good for us and what is due to us – we may never enter into full experience of His plan. There will never be fullness of life in Christ unless we die to our reliance on ourselves.

We can never know His power until we yield to Him, surrender our sovereignty, say a decisive no to unbelief. God wants us, by our acting on the assumption that He is as good as His word, to show to the world that Jesus is the resurrection and the life.

This extract has made me think very deeply about my faith. I know that there are no half measures with God. We all must die to self and totally commit all things to him in good times and bad.

I hope that some day these notes will be of help to someone going through difficult times.

Without God, I am nothing.

I know I still have a long way to go, but with God on my side, I will have the grace and strength to face the days ahead and will keep trusting in the One who gave His life for me. I praise God for all those who love and support me and thank Him for all the prayers said for me through my church and further afield.

To God be the Glory. Amen.

Eleanor Whitcroft
Colorectal Cancer, 2000

My Chemo Tadpoles

Dorothy Dempster
Cervical Cancer, 2000 & Lung Cancer, 2004

My Chemo Tadpoles

I have to tell you a tale about tadpoles.
Tadpoles are the stream of life:
Every little drip goes in,
It springs into life.
They work their way around you,
Killing off the germ
And if you believe in them,
You will live to fight again.

My story could be a long one,
So I will cut it short:
Be strong in mind
As I have been.
Mind over matter,
Mind over pain,
I will live and *hope*
Not to have the fight again.

Dorothy Dempster
Cervical Cancer, 2000 and Lung Cancer, 2004

A New Day

Debbie Green
Throat and Mouth Cancer, 2002 & 2007

Following a year of sore ears and throat infections, a lump eventually appeared on the right side of my neck at the beginning of 2002. Although this lump was found to be malignant, no further action was taken following surgery, as it was considered that there had been no spread.

I continued to suffer similar symptoms however, and so further investigations were undertaken, and in May 2003, it was discovered that this lump was actually the secondary site of a tumour found on the base of my tongue. This was diagnosed as squamous-cell carcinoma. Surgery for this was not a viable option, and therefore the site was treated with seven weeks of radiotherapy, along with two doses of chemotherapy which were administered in the first and fourth weeks.

In the years which followed, I was reviewed regularly by my ENT consultant. In October 2007, a further three small tumours were discovered on the right side of my neck. After much deliberation, my consultant and the Oncologist decided to administer a further six weeks of radiotherapy.

I continue to be kept under review and to date, all follow-up scans have shown no further spread of the cancer.

We will open the book, its pages blank.
We are going to put words on them ourselves.
The book is called Opportunity, and its first chapter is 'A New Day'.

Live simply
Love generously
Care deeply
Speak kindly . . .
Leave the rest to God.

Serenity Prayer
God grant me the serenity to accept the things I cannot change,
The courage to change the things I can,
And the wisdom to know the difference.

To send a letter is a good way to go somewhere without moving anything but your heart.

Avoiding the phrase 'I don't have time...' will soon help you to realise that you do have the time you need for just about anything you choose to accomplish in life.

You must laugh before you are happy, or fear dying, having never laughed.

The two great secrets of happiness: pleasure and oblivion.

You live longer once you realise that time spent being unhappy is time wasted.

Do not dwell on the past; do not dream of the future; concentrate the mind on the present moment.

Debbie Green
Throat and Mouth Cancer, 2002 & 2007

Footprints in the Sand

Robert Bloomer
(Form of) Testicular Cancer, 2005

Hello, my name is Robert Bloomer. Several years ago, I went through a period in my life where I thought I would only have weeks to live. I had been diagnosed with cancer, and had to go through four months of chemotherapy, doing all the scans, blood tests, transfusions, injections, hospital appointments and so on. Along the way, I met many people going through different types of cancer and treatments. I also joined a group in Newtownards called HOPE (**H**elping **O**thers **P**rogress **E**very day), made new friends and listened to many different stories. But through it all, I just wanted to be 'normal' again! This is my story . . .

I was shopping in the Budget DIY store in Bangor one day, when I started to feel very unwell, as if I was going to collapse. I put it down to a lack of food, as I was trying to lose weight at the time. So I went over to McDonalds, had the works and did feel a good bit better. But looking back on it now, I think something was working on me then.

A while later, I moved my mum from Belfast to Bangor, to an apartment not far from us. It was good to have my mum close – she had her own problems, so if anything happened, at least I was nearby. Later my wife and I went on holiday to Italy, to experience the beautiful scenery of the Amalfi coast. I was feeling OK until one day we went on a trip to Mount Vesuvius. As I was walking uphill, I did not feel as fit as I thought I was. Older guys were flying past me and I felt whacked, but was only three-quarters of the way up. Being an ex-firefighter, I thought I was pretty fit!! But I ploughed on to the top anyway.

We came home and I went back to work. At the time I was a driver with Ulsterbus. I was doing a bit of overtime that week, and was feeling very tired and going to the toilet every hour. I put it down to a urinary infection and made an appointment with the doctor for that Friday, in between my shifts. On the Friday, the inspector asked me if I wanted to do more overtime the next day. I remember thinking to myself, 'You're lucky I've been working at all this week, as I have been feeling shattered', but I agreed to do the extra hours anyway. On Friday around lunchtime, I went to the doctor and was given a slip to go and get my bloods done. As there was a long queue in the Treatment room, I decided to leave it until the Monday however. I worked that Saturday, but that weekend I was really feeling rotten, going to the toilet every hour, even during the night, and it was taking a lot out of me. So, in between my shifts on the Monday, my wife Adrienne told me to go down to the GP's surgery to have my bloods done. Once I finished my shift, I headed back to the station from Holywood. To this day, I don't know how the heck I drove home – only the Lord knows that.

After work I went straight home and was on the couch, watching TV with Adrienne and taking it easy, when the phone rang. It was a doctor telling me that my blood results were showing a high level of calcium and advising me to go to A & E so they could check me out. Well, talk about feeling physically sick! We went up to A & E and I was given a bed, and before I knew it, doctors were all around me. Alarm bells rang in my head: you don't normally get so many doctors round one patient, unless they are worried about something.

I remember one doctor had long locks and all I could think about was Engelbert Humperdinck! The other doctor, as I remember it, was very eccentric, with a dickey bow on, and I thought, 'Why the heck would these guys be down at A & E looking at me when you normally just get a junior doctor?' They prodded me around my tummy, mumbled to each other and then did a bit more pushing and feeling. The nerves started to flow through my body, and I was thinking, 'This doesn't look good'.

The doctors went away, and then Engelbert Humperdinck came back to talk to me. I said to him, 'OK, doctor. What does a high calcium level mean? It must point to something, right?' He was very honest and to the point, replying, 'It is about 99 per cent likely that it is cancer. There is a mass in your abdomen, and I am surprised actually that you have not collapsed with this calcium level.' My first thought was that I had just been driving buses around!

From A & E, I went to Ward Four, in a room of my own. I know Adrienne was as worried as I was. The nurses were very good and I was told I would be staying for some tests, etc. It did not take a rocket scientist to work out what type of ward I was in, and weighing everything up, I did not think I would ever see the outside world and breathe the air there again. Life seemed so precious at that point, and all I could think about were the many things I wanted to do – it was a big list. I also thought about how Adrienne and our lads would cope. We take life for granted so much and put things off till tomorrow, instead of living life today as the gift that it is – but that's human nature, I suppose.

So, I settled down as best I could – well, I didn't have many other options, really. I got a chest X-ray and various other tests the next day. I was allowed out of hospital that weekend, but had to be back in again on the Sunday.

The second week, I went for a CAT scan (no, not a cat walking over me and having a look!), something I had always been afraid of having to going through. But I had to face up to it and a lot more fears in the weeks to come. Before going for the scan, I was given a drink to take: it tasted of aniseed and looked a bit like orange juice. Adrienne came down to the scan room with me and to give me some moral support. I remember sitting in the corridor outside that room, shaking all over and wondering what would show up. A droning noise was coming from inside the room, and this made my mind work overtime too.

The door opened and a nurse brought me into the scan room. There was a machine in there which was like a big doughnut with a bed in the middle. To one side were the TV screens which the nurses and doctors would look at as you were being scanned. I was told to lie down on the bed. For other scans I was to have after this one, I was given an injection each time beforehand: the stuff they injected me with made me feel as if I had wet myself – a weird feeling. I do not remember getting such an injection for this first scan, but so much was going through my head at that stage, perhaps I just didn't notice. I think though they may have been worried about my kidneys at first, and so perhaps didn't want to give me the injection in case they damaged anything.

Anyway, the nurse who had brought me into the room left, and then the big doughnut seemed to start going round, making a loud noise. A voice came from a speaker above me, telling me to, 'Breathe in and hold, please', then I was moved through the doughnut until it stopped and then the voice said, 'Breathe out'. This was done a couple of times. When I looked over to my left, I could see the doctor and nurses looking at the screens, a couple of them with very worried looking faces, which made me feel very uneasy. I was completely alone, and after what seemed like forever, a nurse came out, unstrapped me and told me to go back to the seat outside, to wait for the porter to come down. I told Adrienne about the nurses' faces looking worried, but she told me not to fret, and that it was probably all in my mind.

I was then taken back to the ward again, where more blood was taken. Adrienne left later that afternoon to go home to see the boys. Left alone, I started thinking a lot. It is hard, being on your own in this type of situation; your mind wanders all over the place. I started to pray and ask the Lord to forgive all my sins and to wash them away. I also asked Him to help me through and help me face my fear, and from that moment on, I felt more relaxed – as if I knew that the Lord would be with me through whatever was sent my way.

The next day Adrienne came to see me again, and while she was there, around lunchtime, the doctor with the dickey bow came in with his head down, looking as if he had something to tell me. He said I had a large mass in my abdomen which seemed to be just sitting there, apparently not attached to anything. He then said he wanted me to have a bone scan and a chest X-ray, and so on, and he had another feel around my stomach. During the next few days, other doctors came in and examined me – I felt that I was either very important or just a guinea pig! Each day which followed was the same: the doctor with the dickey bow would come in, looking glum and with no more information for me. But I felt somehow more relaxed, knowing the Lord was with me.

I was still anxious though to know what exactly it was I was facing. Not knowing anything was the worst thing of all. I am sure that the doctors did not know much more than what they had told me, and I suppose it was a good thing that they did so many tests to be sure about how – and if – they could treat me, but I was wanting answers right away. It is often hard to get doctors to talk to you on a level playing field, and it is true that some do not treat you as a human being. But they gave me all the tests anyway and assured me that staying in the hospital would make these tests quicker. Yet I, of course, was busting to get home and back to normal and, to me, feeling like this was a good sign, I thought . . .

Near the end of the week, I had an appointment to go and have a bone scan at Belvoir Hospital. Adrienne and I drove over to the hospital, and as we walked round to the reception, we passed old stores and work places that made me feel this place was trapped in a time warp – everything seemed so dreary and old-fashioned. Anyway, I was called into a room and given an injection to prepare me for the bone scan – I was then told to go away and come back about an hour later. So we went and had a coffee and a wee drive and headed back, coming up to the hour. I was called into a sizeable room containing another bed with a large scanner connected to it. I lay down on the bed: there were two guys sitting to my left, where the screen and other equipment were situated. As they chatted to me, they worked the scanner over me very slowly. The room was very hollow and intimidating, and it all seemed to last forever. I was glad when it was over and we were able to go back to the Ulster hospital, where I was settled back into the ward. Being in a room by myself had its good and bad points. You never got to know many people or what was happening on the ward – but I presume that on this type of ward, people need their own space anyway.

I got home at the weekend again, and boy did I dread going back in to hospital again – but I had no choice, of course. On the Monday morning the doctor with the dickey bow (a nice man, but who didn't usually have much to say) told me he was sending me to have a biopsy that afternoon. When the time came, I was wheeled down in my bed to the ultrasound room where I was having the biopsy: there wasn't much space to turn the bed round into the room! One of the young student nurses came down with me: she was very good, as were all the nurses on the ward.

The doctor prepared the equipment for the biopsy. I did feel very nervous as to what was going to happen, but he explained what I could expect to happen. He proceeded to numb the area where he was going to do the small op, and then he pushed a long instrument into me (not musical instrument like a guitar or anything, though!). There was a gripper on the end which he would use to take a bit of the tumour for examination. It was uncomfortable at first, but when he went in deeper and tried to take a bit of the tumour, it was actually painful, so he stopped and injected more anaesthetic around the area. He tried again and got a chunk of the tumour – thank God! – he brought this out and put it onto a tray to be sent away. He then got cleaned up and patched up the wound, and the nurse came back to take me back to the ward. The biopsy was sure an experience! The area was very uncomfortable for a few days, but the nurses kept a good eye on it.

I loved getting home at the weekends. When I was home one weekend, I happened to open my father's Bible at the page marker, which had not been moved since he died in 1999. My eyes fell on the words, from Jeremiah 30:17, "'For I will restore health unto thee and I will heal thee of thy wounds," saith the Lord.' To me, it was like my dad was talking to me and I got some comfort from this. Odd, the marker being at that page and my eyes falling on this verse. Many such things happened during my illness, like signs that I was being looked after and that I should not worry.

The days passed, and the doctor with the dickey bow came in most mornings, still with a worried face and no more information about me or what they were dealing with. So many things went through my head when I was in hospital for those 3 weeks: worry; all the things I still wanted to do; questions about why God had let this happen to me; how long did I have; how would Adrienne and my sons cope . . . There is so much that you think about, but I got comfort from praying and, with a little reading of my dad's Bible, I knew that God did not do this to me. And I knew He was with me, no matter what.

As I have said, word back about the biopsy seemed to take forever. But one morning when Adrienne was with me (as she always tried to be: she was truly a tower of strength to me, then and always), my friend with the dickey bow came in, and he actually had a smile on his face! 'Well,' he said, 'You have a semi-noma tumour and we can treat this type of testicular cancer.' It seemed so much of a relief for him that he finally knew what they were dealing with – and such a relief for us that I had a chance of survival! He told us that I would have radiotherapy, as semi-nomas respond well to this treatment. He also said that it was good that they had taken the time to find out which type of tumour they were treating, as they could now give me the correct treatment.

The next day, I was all dressed to go home, and just waiting for the information about where and when I would be getting my treatment. Then the nurse came over and informed me that I was to have chemotherapy – a bit of a shock, as the doctor had said radiotherapy, but the nurse said that had changed, and that I would be having chemotherapy at Belvoir Hospital. I was to go there on the Monday of the following week, and it sure was a worry, thinking about what would happen when I got the chemotherapy: how would I react, how would I look, and so on? The word chemotherapy is mentioned and so many pictures go through your head. But of course it was good news that they could treat the cancer at all, so I kept reminding myself of this plus point.

Monday came and we headed up to Belvoir. On the ward we went to, people were all walking about, connected to machines and drips: you could hear bleeping sounds and see nurses going over to people and working with the machines to stop the bleeping. Some of the drip pouches had black bags over them: I found out later that the patients with these were being given chemotherapy. You could see nurses putting gloves on when changing the chemo bags on the drips.

Once I was weighed and my blood pressure taken and bloods done, I was given a bed and a doctor came round to give me information on the type of chemo I was going to be given. Then he asked me to sign a form to say I was agreeing to have the chemo and that I was aware that the treatment could kill me. So I was having something to help me, which could kill me at the same time! Well I was there, so I wanted to get started. The possible side effects worried me a bit, but at least I was getting treatment!

First, I was put on a drip to flush out my system. I was hooked up to a monitor, which was set to measure the exact amount of fluid to be given. It was very daunting and scary, with all the monitors going. A guy beside me was sick with the chemo he was being given – which was the same as mine, so I was not looking forward to that bit! After a couple of bags of different fluids, the nurse finally came round that night with the chemo for me. To hook me up, she had to put gloves on and she also had a black bag to put over the chemo bag, to let them know I was on the juice!

When I was hooked up to the chemo, my body seemed to brace itself. This was one of the two types of chemo I was to get. I was told one of them can give you nausea; I was also told that I would lose my hair, and they could even tell me more or less the exact date my hair would go! As a man, this did not worry me so much – well, that's what I thought at the time. I was not as sick as the guy beside me – I felt some nausea, but it wasn't too bad. I was in for four days, and home on the Thursday. I got to know a few people on the ward. The food was not very good, and the smell from the drains from the toilets was not very pleasant. Apparently, they were running the place down, as they were moving to a new centre in Belfast City Hospital.

At home again on the Friday, I felt ok and went for a spin with Adrienne. We walked around a few shops in Bangor, and I also got my hair cut – down to a number two! As the girl was cutting, it was a bit painful, as the hair cells must have been starting to die already. I had to ask her to take it easy and when I told her why, she sure slowed up! After that, we called into a Christian bookshop on High Street, where my eyes fell upon a CD – *Healing Rain* by Michael M. Smith. I bought it there and then, and the song 'Healing Rain' stuck with me. There was also a song that was in the charts at the time, called 'Wake Me up When September Ends' by the group Green Day: this song seemed so relevant to me, since my chemotherapy would end around September!

On the Saturday of that first weekend after chemo, I was helping Karl and Phillip wash the car and feeling ok, when I became very weak and needed to go in and lie down. I lay down for a while and started to shiver, even though I did not feel cold. Adrienne took my temperature and it was high, so she phoned the hospital and they said I should come up so they could check me out. Of course that was the last place I wanted to go: I had just got home and wanted to stay with my family until the next treatment! But I knew I did not feel great, and the shivering was getting worse. So we went up to Belvoir and round to the ward where I had been given the chemo. One of the nurses came and took my blood, and said I was looking a bit pale, which was not great news for me. A doctor came over and had a talk with me: he said that if my bloods were low, they might have to keep me in. I was feeling very weak by then, and knew that I would be staying. But the thought of not going home got me well pissed off!

About 30 minutes or so later, the doctor came back with the news: 'Well, your bloods are very low. You have caught an infection and it would be very dangerous to let you go home.' So I got a bed and tried my best to settle down. My temperature was high and I was shivering. They gave me antibiotics by injection, and put a fan beside my bed to cool me down, as I was feeling really bad. The next day, they moved me to another room. I was really feeling very low. I seemed to go downhill a bit from there, and the following day, after two bed moves, I felt as if the life was draining from me. I remember saying to Mary, one of the nurses who was working on me, that I felt so weak and drained, I really did think I was going to die. As she administered some more drugs to me, Mary's reply was simply, 'You will be like a new man soon!'

Low and behold, about three hours later, I started to feel a lot better: Mary was so right! Karl my son came up to see me in the afternoon, and I sure was feeling a bit perkier. Later that afternoon however, I was feeling very down and so a nurse came to sit with me. I was reminiscing about my life, and this nurse was so good to listen to me, talking and crying and so on. The nurses in that ward are fantastic – we do not appreciate what they do. Often we only complain, but I cannot thank them enough for the care they gave me.

Once I felt a bit better and I seemed to be stabilised, my bloods were still not good, so they had to give me a blood transfusion. This was another fear I had had: taking someone else's blood. But now I know that without people giving blood, a lot more people could die – so a big thank you to whoever it was that gave me blood, and a thank you also to everyone who donates blood.

Anyway, the doctors came round to see me again. I was complaining about a sharp pain on my right side, so one of the doctors recommended that a CAT scan should be done, as there was a fear I might have appendicitis. A couple of days later, my consultant and another doctor came round to see me: they had good news from the scan! It did not show any appendicitis, but it did show that my tumour had reduced dramatically in size – by more than half. So the chemo was doing its job, which was great to know and gave me more strength to carry on.

Another thing the doctors mentioned to me that day was in relation to injections to keep my white cell count up. Really I should have been given these injections after the first chemo session, but I think money comes into it a lot, so they had let me go without, probably to see how much my bloods would fall. If my cell counts had been ok, then they might not even have mentioned the possibility of getting such injections – you just wonder. Anyway, they were now saying that they would be giving me ten of the injections, so that I might be able to avoid an infection next time. It was either have a nurse come out every day, or Adrienne could do it. Adrienne said she would do it, and I must say it was very brave of her. The nurse later showed Adrienne how to inject the Nupregen (into my tummy in this case). At the end of that week, I was able to go home again. It was so good to get home, even though there was not long to go before I would be getting my next chemo treatment.

The next couple of weeks flew in and before I knew it, I was back in to get my next dose of chemo. On the ward, I was always aware that there are so many people going through so many different types of treatment, and just getting on with it – through pain, loneliness, depression and all the other emotions that go through your mind and the dramatic things that happen to your body. You just have to get on with it and look forward to getting home again. The thought of the chemo going through my body was always scary, but it is so good that they can treat you in some way. The food though just got worse but, when they only have about 90 pence for every patient, what do you expect?

I got to know a few of the other patients when I was in over the next few months. One gentleman, in the bed in front of me, was having a rough time with the radiotherapy he was having around his lower half and he was up during the night a lot going to the toilet: it took a lot out of him. Another guy, in the bed beside me, was on his second dose of chemo and he suffered a lot from sickness – but, like us all, he never complained much, just got on with it. It was always so great to get out again and breathe the fresh air after a treatment. When you're healthy with no worries, you never appreciate nature and your surroundings. We live such a fast life, in which people have no time for anything, it seems.

With the chemo, I found that everything I would eat, even at home, was tasteless. Steaks were like cardboard; even water tasted funny. One thing I love is chocolate, but the chemo made the chocolate taste so sweet, I was put off eating it. Pity it did not stay with me though (the overly sweet taste, not the chemo, I mean!). So I found I ate more savoury meals – beans, spuds, bangers with loads of brown sauce, kebabs . . . Even MacDonald's tasted good compared with other foods. After the first month, when I lost a bit of weight, I started to put it back on again, with all the wrong foods.

A few days before I was going back in for another stay in hospital for more chemo, I started to feel weak again, so I had to get another blood transfusion. In fact, I had to do this every time just before I got chemo, and when I got the blood, it sure did help. Adrienne managed well, injecting me with the Nupergen, which helped keep my bloods just high enough so I could go ahead with the chemo. I had four sessions of chemo altogether.

During the treatments and when I was in hospital, I read a couple of books which helped. One was about Lance Armstrong and his fight with cancer. I was having the same chemo as he had had, and it sure was hard on my body. Lance Armstrong went through a lot more than I did though, and seeing what he did after it all gave me strength. I also bought a book called *Taming the Tiger*, a very good read about a guy who becomes a Christian and about how life is not easy but that to have the Lord with you gives you the strength to know that, no matter what happens, it will be all ok. A lot of things happen in our lives that sometimes are out of our control, and to have faith, no matter what, does help you to get by, day by day.

I often think of a poem called 'Footprints' by Carolyn Carty, which I think has a lot of truth to it. This is how it goes:

One night a man had a dream. He dreamed he was walking along the beach with the Lord. Across the sky flashed scenes from his life. For each scene, he noticed two sets of footprints in the sand: one belonging to him, and the other to the Lord.

When the last scene of his life flashed before him, he looked back at the footprints in the sand. He noticed that many times along the path of his life there was only one set of footprints. He also noticed it happened at the very lowest and saddest times of his life.

This really bothered him and he questioned the Lord about it: 'Lord, you said that, once I decided to follow you, you'd walk with me all the way. But I have noticed that during the most troublesome times in my life, there is only one set of footprints. I don't understand why, when I needed you most, you would leave me.'

The Lord replied, 'My precious, precious child, I love you and I would never leave you. During your times of trial and suffering, when you see only one set of footprints, it was then that I carried you.'

Many things happened through my treatment, and I do believe my guardian angel – someone – was watching over me, giving me strength to face what ever happened.

Just as I got my mum living close by to us, I took ill myself and so was unable to go round to see her as much as I would have liked. But luckily Adrienne, Karl, and Phillip helped out a lot. When all my treatment was finished and I started to get back to normal, my mum started to feel unwell, sadly. I took her to the doctor, and they said it might be a urine infection, but mum was not getting any better. She fell one day in her living room, but got to the phone to call us, and we got there to find her lying on the floor. At A & E, they checked her over and the doctor was thinking of keeping my mum in overnight, but she was sure not having it, so they eventually told her it was ok to go home again. She was delighted, but I was worried at the time.

We went on holiday and my Aunt Kathy said she would keep an eye on my mum. This was reassuring: Kathy did a lot for my mum and was a good friend. (My mum appreciated all that she did, and I will also always be very grateful to Kathy.) A few days into our holiday, I got a text from Kathy to say that my mum had fallen again and was being taken into hospital. I spoke to Mum and she seemed ok about it all. I said I would try and get home, but she told me to wait, as it was just a couple more days till I got home. I said I loved her and would see her soon. When I got home, we went up to the hospital and my mum was lying in bed, a bit depressed. It seemed that no one was helping her, even though she was complaining of a pain in her back a lot. Any time I went up, the nurses were not doing too much around the ward. From what I could see, it seemed to be a hassle for some of those nurses if they had to do something for the patients.

We got my mum home, but she was a bit down, to say the least: she could hardly walk. We set up carers to come three times a day to help her get back her strength and of course we visited her often ourselves. Not long after Mum was back home from hospital, Adrienne and I were taking a drive when she phoned me, and we said we would call round to her on our way back. When we got there, I opened the door to my mum's apartment and heard her shouting for me. We ran to the bathroom and my mum was there on the floor: she was not a good colour. As I tried to reassure her, Adrienne phoned 999. The First Response team was very fast getting there, but when the ambulance guys were working on my mum, she seemed to drift away. I heard one of the guys say he could not get any blood pressure. So they took Mum straight to hospital, and we followed behind.

When we got to A & E, we were able to go straight to see Mum. A doctor said to me that she had a large blood clot in her lung, and that it was serious: all they could do was inject a blood clot disperser, but it was very risky at my mum's age. I explained all this to her, and she said she wanted them to go ahead anyway: she just wanted rid of the pain. These were the last words my mum said – within minutes, they were giving her CPR. I phoned my mum's pastor, Billy, who came up to the hospital at once. He said a prayer with us.

This had all happened so fast, and I often wonder why it was not picked up on earlier.

Throughout my treatment, my mum always said I would be ok. I sometimes wonder if she didn't pray to the Lord to ask Him to take her instead of me. Mum did miss my dad a lot and at least now they are together once again. I also miss my dad greatly: I miss being able to talk to him man-to-man, son to dad, and just hearing his advice or his opinion on things. I wonder about what he would have said to me when my wife Adrienne was going through cancer herself (Adrienne was diagnosed with breast cancer in 2001). I know he would have been a great support to me, but I also know he was with me in spirit then, and always. My mum took on the role of mother and father when my Dad died, and she was always so positive to me and Adrienne. I feel I did not say 'I love you' enough, or thank her enough for all she did for me throughout my life.

I do get angry with God sometimes, for taking away my mum, just as I had moved her to live close to me, and just as I got better. But at least I know that she loved living in Bangor. My mum and dad and other members of the family are buried at Moneyreagh, a place my dad loved and always wanted to live in.

Thankfully, it is almost six years now since I was diagnosed and I am pleased to say that I am in good health. I still have regular checkups and scans and I hope that my health will continue to be good.

I want to say a big thank you to all the nurses and doctors and the many other people I have come across during my treatment. Most were very good – although some seem to have forgotten that they are human, and do not listen or talk to you as another human being: communication is a very important thing! Adrienne has been a tower of strength through everything, including going through her own treatment and being there for mine – as have my sons, Phillip and Karl. I am sure it was hard for them, but they gave me strength to carry on at the most difficult times. And just to wake up every day is the Lord's blessing.

CATASTROPHIC!
ANXIOUS!
NO TASTE!
CRISIS!
EXHAUSTED!
RETURNING TO "NORMAL"!

How Lonely It Can Be

Sitting in our Home with Ade
A phone call to make life fade
Lying in A&E feeling like an experiment
Why me, Lord, why me?
How lonely it can be.

Sign the form, Chemo on the way
How will my body react on that day?
Where did all my hair go!
I feel so low
How lonely it can be.

Bubble

Where did the family go?
What happened to the bubble?
It had burst.
See you in three months was the last I heard.
Oh dear I am on my own
The Hospital
Yes I missed the Hospital (The Bubble)
All the care
All the treatment
All the Nurses
I must face the outside now
Back to normal, my normal
Oh dear I am on my own.

Robert Bloomer
(Form of) Testicular Cancer, 2005

Teach Me to Dance

Roslyn Wilson
Sarcoma of the Uterus, 2003

Roslyn Wilson joined the HOPE Cancer Support Group when it was founded in 2006, and remained a valued member until her death in July 2010. The inspirational text below was given to us by Roslyn's husband, Leslie, and was something which Roslyn put together for a talk she gave at a meeting of her church's women's group, Interflo, in 2005.

When I attended a Life in the Spirit Seminar here in West (Bangor West Presbyterian Church) over 23 years ago, the words of Jesus, 'I have come, so you might have life in abundance', had a profound effect on me. Prior to that, I had existed as a Christian with no real relationship with Jesus. After that Seminar, a personal relationship developed which has grown up over the years. In spite of all the ups and downs, today I am a work-in-progress, by God's grace.

A year ago this month, I was diagnosed with a rare form of cancer in the muscle of my womb, but I want to share with you that throughout the eight months of treatment I experienced 'life in all its abundance'.

When the doctor explained my illness to me and all the treatment to follow, I just sat there, outwardly calm but inwardly numb. Cancer never entered my mind – I had expected a hysterectomy operation. When Leslie and I escaped to the car, we just sat and 'bawled our eyes out' and later, with our two daughters and sons-in-law, we were able to comfort and support each other. Fiona Castles has said that cancer is a word, not a sentence, and my testimony is that in spite of my weakness of faith, God in His love uses the circumstances for His purposes and for my own spiritual growth.

'God's ways are not our ways, neither are His thoughts our thoughts' – so I have read in the Bible, but I experienced this as I packed my case, ready for my second chemotherapy treatment. My regime was to spend four days every three weeks in Belvoir (Park Hospital). As I packed, I said, 'Lord, I don't want to go again – I know this time what the treatment involves and although it is not painful, I would rather give it a miss.' Immediately the thought came – 'Treat it like a holiday'.

Now, who would say that going into hospital is like going on holiday?!

But my attitude changed, as I allowed this thought to take hold. In the days that followed and throughout the rest of my treatment, my holiday adventure took me to Belvoir, where I met very special people and, in God's timing, I was able to share about my faith and the prayerful support of all the people in the West. One of those special people was a lovely Christian doctor, Heather (who was gentle like heather). Often, after a visit from my consultant and her team, this special doctor would come back to my bed and ask if I had understood what had been said. She would then proceed to explain – often drawing diagrams – about the treatment in a way I could understand. Over the months, we shared about our faith, and I told her I prayed for her and she also told me that she went to Mass each day and prayed for her patients. After my third treatment of chemotherapy, a CT bone scan revealed that the tumour had reduced by 50 per cent, and was nowhere else in my body.

On one of her visits to the hospital, my daughter Louise was telling me that Darren, her husband, had bought a tent so that the family could go camping in the future. Cathryn, their four-and-a-half-year-old daughter, was so excited and asked if Daddy would put up the tent in the back garden for one night, so that she could sleep in it with him. Cathryn, equipped with her sandwiches for supper, spent the night in the tent and enjoyed the experience. The Lord used that to show me that Cathryn was able to sleep in the tent, totally secure in her father's protection: she was not afraid of the dark or of the wind blowing – she was with her father. As for me, I was to have that child-like trust also, and rest secure in my Heavenly Father's love.

Often it is when you are trying to get off to sleep that the 'what if' thoughts come to mind – for example, what if the tumour gets bigger, what if it spreads, and so on. I am slowly learning to deal with these negatives – to nip them in the bud before they do any damage! God has given us His resources, one of which is His Word, which is described as 'the Sword of the Spirit'. This is a powerful tool and one I would encourage you to keep using. When these thoughts occur, I repeat out loud verses of Scripture and keep on allowing these verses to permeate my body, mind and spirit, until His peace comes and I drift off to sleep: verses such as: Proverbs 3: 5–8: 'Trust in the Lord with all your heart and do not lean on your own understanding. In all your ways, acknowledge Him and He will direct your path. Be wise not in your own eyes, fear the Lord and turn away from evil. It will be healing to your flesh and refreshment to your bones'; or Jeremiah 17: 7, 8: 'Blessed is the man who trusts in the Lord. He is like a tree planted by water and does not fear when the heat comes, for its leaves remain green, and is not anxious in the year of drought, for it does not cease to bear fruit.' All of us here tonight have known difficult times and I'm sure like me, you have appreciated the love and support of God's people upholding us in these times. Often a telephone call, a card or someone calling was just what was needed to refresh and equip us. Thank you.

So, what of the future? I have a CT scan on Friday and see the consultant in April. I do not know what lies ahead . . . And to be honest, part of me is scared, but – and this is the important part – I am holding on to the One who knows and that brings deep contentment.

Before I finish, I must tell you what happened last Sunday evening at church. I arrived over early, and noticed that the last song to finish the service was 'Teach Me to Dance'. I had brought praise tapes into hospital with me, and this song had lifted my spirits on many occasions. During the service, the thought came: 'Take a flag and dance in worship before me'. After Heather finished speaking about the valley of the dry bones of Ezekiel, Eileen led us in a celebration dance, finishing up at the front of the church with many young – and not so young! – people joining in. Immediately after this, Paul Shields started to play 'Teach Me to Dance', and I saw a beautiful flag with the word 'Hallelujah' on it. I lifted it and started to worship. When I came home, I remembered the prophetic word which had been given to my husband Leslie when I was at my weakest last year – Ballycastle, 3 August 2004 – 8.20 a.m.: 'Blessed are they that dance in the Lord, for they shall be fully restored'.

So, if the Lord asks you to wave a flag in church, forget about people – just obey and do it!

Roslyn Wilson
Sarcoma of the Uterus, 2003

HOPE Generic Cancer Support Group

HOPE Generic Cancer Support Group

The HOPE (**H**elping **O**thers **P**rogress **E**very Day) Cancer Support Group was established in 2006 by Kathy Cash and Susan Wilson, as the first *generic* group of its kind to have been set up – i.e. not exclusively for those suffering from one specific type of cancer. The group's purpose is to offer support and encouragement to anyone whose life has been affected by cancer – regardless of which form the illness takes –by creating opportunities for them to meet others going through similar experiences, and to share and discuss issues of concern.

Aims and Objectives of the group

We run the group according to our members' needs, in a clear and accountable manner. We welcome everyone equally and take steps to make the group open and accessible. We ensure that all members can participate in running the group and are involved in decision-making. We make sure that everyone understands and respects the importance of confidentiality. We undertake to listen to each other and respond with sensitivity at all times.

We offer:

- informal group discussion
- emotional support
- informed, practical support
- talks by professionals on cancer-related issues

Other activities offered for members by the HOPE Group include:-

- working together to create and maintain our 'Garden of Reflection', situated at the Kiltonga Nature Reserve (the 'Duck Pond'), Newtownards.
- Creative writing
- Art therapy
- Social outings
- Fundraising events

Group meetings are held on the last Wednesday of the month at the Link Family and Community Centre in Newtownards, from 7 p.m. until 8.30 p.m.

Contact details for further information:

The Link Family and Community Centre
10 West Street
Newtownards BT23 4EN
Telephone: 02891821124
Email: info@thelinkcentre.org

Kathy Cash, The HOPE Generic Cancer Support Group
Telephone: 02891814410
Email: kathycash3@hotmail.com